GCSE AQA Double Award
Applied Science
The Workbook

This book is for anyone doing **GCSE AQA Applied Science (Double Award)**
at foundation level.

GCSE Science is all about **understanding how science works**.
And not only that — understanding it well enough to be able to **question**
what you hear on TV and read in the papers.

But you can't do that without a fair chunk of **background knowledge**. Hmm, tricky.

This book is full of **tricky questions**... each one designed to make you sweat
— because that's the only way you'll get any **better**.

There are questions to see **what facts** you know. There are questions to see how
well you can **apply those facts**. And there are questions to see how well you
understand the role of **scientists** in the **real world**.

It's also got some daft bits in to try and make the whole
experience at least vaguely entertaining for you.

What CGP is all about

Our sole aim here at CGP is to produce the highest
quality books — carefully written, immaculately presented
and dangerously close to being funny.

Then we work our socks off to get them
out to you — at the cheapest possible prices.

Contents

SECTION 2.6 — CHEMICAL BUILDING BLOCKS

SECTION 2.7 — MATERIALS FOR CONSTRUCTION

SECTION 2.8 — SCIENCE IN THE HOME

SECTION 2.9 — TRANSPORT

SECTION 2.10 — COMMUNICATION DEVICES

Published by Coordination Group Publications Ltd.

Editors:
Amy Boutal, Ellen Bowness, Tom Cain, Katherine Craig, Kate Houghton,
Rose Parkin, Katherine Reed, Rachel Selway, Laurence Stamford.

Contributors:
Derek Harvey, Judith Hayes, Dr Giles R Greenway, Barbara Mascetti,
Andy Rankin, Philip Rushworth, Claire Stebbing, Sophie Watkins.

ISBN: 978 1 84146 775 7

With thanks to Jeremy Cooper, Ian Francis, Sue Hocking, Ami Snelling,
Jennifer Underwood and Sarah Williams for the proofreading.
With thanks to Laura Phillips for the copyright research.

Graph on page 19 courtesy of National Human Genome Research Institute.

Data on page 38 reproduced with kind permission from the British Heart Foundation © 2007.

Data on page 59 reproduced with kind permission from the Pew Initiative on Food and Biotechnology.
Factsheet: Genetically Modified Crops in the United States.

Data for Graph on page 73 reproduced with kind permission from Earth System Research
Laboratory, National Oceanic and Atmospheric Administration, and Scripps Institution of
Oceanography, University of California.

Groovy website: www.cgpbooks.co.uk

Printed by Elanders Hindson Ltd, Newcastle upon Tyne.
Jolly bits of clipart from CorelDRAW®

Organisms and Cells

Q1   Dr Hilder is a **pathologist**. Much of his job involves looking at samples of
cells under the microscope to find out if there is anything wrong with them.
The diagram below shows some **humans cells** observed by Dr Hilder.

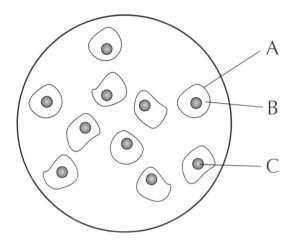

a)   Draw lines to match parts A, B and C of the cells shown above with the correct names.

A	nucleus
B	cell membrane
C	cytoplasm

b)   Complete the table below to match each description with the correct part (A, B or C) of the cell.

Part of cell	Description
	Determines the characteristics of the individual with these cells.
	This is where most chemical reactions take place.
	Controls what goes in and out of the cell.

c)   Dr Hilder works in a laboratory. List two things he should do to reduce his risk of injury.

1. ....

2. ....

Top Tips: All living things are made up of cells — they're the very basic 'building blocks' of
life. So it's really pretty fundamental for you to know what they contain and how they allow us to
function. Cells make up all the tissues, organs and systems in our bodies.

Specialised Cells

Q1   A **haematologist** is a scientist who studies **blood**. Haematologists
must use **safe procedures** when handling samples of blood.

a)   Red and white blood cells are specialised cells that perform different functions.
Explain how the following features make the blood cells better adapted to their function.

i)   Red blood cells are small, flexible and have a biconcave shape.

....

....

ii) Red blood cells contain no nucleus.

....

iii) Some white blood cells are flexible and some can produce antibodies.

....

....

b)   Give one precaution that a haematologist would have to
take when analysing blood samples in the laboratory.

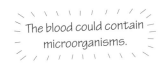
The blood could contain microorganisms.

....

Q2   **Nerve cells** can be examined under the microscope. Scientists who study the
nervous system are called **neuroscientists**. The diagram below shows a nerve cell.

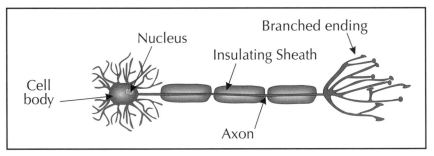

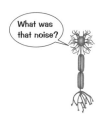
What was that noise?

a)   Complete the paragraph below using some of the words in the box.

slows down	electrical impulses	speeds up	nucleus	electrical	axon

Nerve cells (neurones) transmit information around the body as ....

These pass along the .... of the cell. The insulating sheath acts as an

.... insulator, which .... the impulse.

b)   What is the function of the branched endings?

....

<u>Diffusion and Osmosis in Cells</u>

Q1   **Lucy** is a world famous **athlete** and she is running in a marathon.

a)   Tick the correct boxes to show whether the statements below are **true** or **false**.

		True	False
i)	Oxygen moves into Lucy's muscles from the blood by osmosis.	☐	☐
ii)	Oxygen moves into Lucy's blood from the air in the lungs by diffusion.	☐	☐
iii)	Water in Lucy's stomach moves into her blood by osmosis.	☐	☐
iv)	The products of digestion move from the digestive system into the blood by osmosis.	☐	☐

b)   Osmosis and diffusion are taking place all the time in Lucy's body.
Draw lines to match each statement with the process(es) it describes.

Only involves movement of water molecules.

Involves movement of particles from high concentration to low concentration.

Osmosis

Diffusion

Q2   Nick drinks some juice that contains a high concentration of **sugar**.

a)   The juice enters Nick's stomach and moves through to the small intestine.
Choose words from the list to complete the passage explaining what happens to the juice next.
Each word may be used once, more than once or not at all.

diffusion	lower	osmosis	higher	nerves	blood

Water enters the blood by .... It is then carried

around the body by the .... Sugar enters the blood by

.... When it reaches cells with a ....

sugar concentration than the blood, it enters them by ....

b)   Diagrams A and B below show the concentration of sugar in Nick's small intestine and blood after he drinks the juice. Write down the order in which they occur.

Key	
🐚	Water molecule
🔘	Glucose molecule

A   Small intestine   Blood

B   Small intestine   Blood

Correct order: 1. ...., 2. ....

Respiration

Q1   Doctor Smith is a **sports scientist**. He's investigating how the activity of athletes affects their rate of respiration.

a)   Explain what is meant by the term **respiration**.

....

b)   Complete the following word equation for respiration:

glucose + ... → **carbon dioxide** + ...

c)   Give three things that the energy released by respiration is used for.

....

....

d)   In one experiment he measures the **amount of oxygen** that enters the blood from the lungs per unit time for an athlete before, during and after a 4000 m run. A graph of his results is shown below.

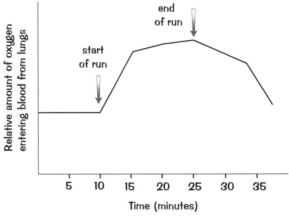

i)   Describe the change in the rate of oxygen absorption into the blood over the 35 minutes.

....

....

ii)   Why do you think there was a change in the rate of oxygen absorption during the race?

....

e)   In the body, the pathway that oxygen takes from the air to the cells occurs in three stages. Complete the sentences below to show what happens.

i)   Breathing in moves oxygen into the ....

ii)   Oxygen then .... into the blood.

iii)   Blood moves around the .... system to all cells, supplying them with oxygen for respiration.

The Blood

Q1   A **doctor** took a sample of **blood** from a patient and analysed it.
The results of his analysis are shown below.

> Number of red blood cells per mm³ = 6 million
>
> Number of white blood cells per mm³ = 6000
>
> Number of platelets per mm³ = 100 000

a)   How many times more red blood cells are there, than white blood cells?

....

b)   **i)**   What is the name of the liquid that carries platelets, red blood cells and white blood cells around in the blood?

....

ii)   Name two other substances that are transported by this liquid.

1. ....

2. ....

c)   The doctor concluded that the platelet count was lower than average in this patient.
How might this affect the patient?

....

d)   What is the role of the white blood cells?

....

Q2   **Red blood cells** are one of the main components of blood.

Fill in the missing words in the passage below to describe the function of red blood cells.

lungs	haemoglobin	oxyhaemoglobin	oxygen	body cells

Red blood cells contain the chemical ....

When the red blood cells pass through the capillaries next to the

.... this chemical reacts with oxygen to form

.... In the body cells, the reverse happens and

.... releases ....

The Circulatory System

Q1   Toby has recently been experiencing **chest pains** — his GP referred him to a **cardiologist**. The cardiologist explained to Toby how blood flow in his body depends on the health of his heart and the diameter of his blood vessels.

a)   **i)**   Draw arrows on the diagram to show the flow of blood through Toby's brain.

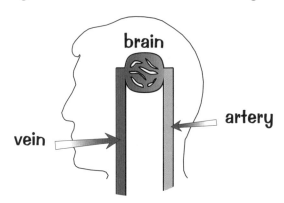

ii)   Give one difference between the blood flowing through this artery and the blood flowing through this vein.

....

....

b)   Fill in the blanks in the passage below using words from the box.

vein	vena cava	deoxygenated	aorta	artery	oxygenated	double

Humans have a .... circulatory system. In the first circuit, blood is

pumped from the heart to the lungs through the pulmonary .... and

then back to the heart through the pulmonary .... In the second

circuit, ... blood leaves the heart through the ....

.... blood returns to the heart through the ....

c)   What is the function of the heart?

....

d)   What is the function of capillaries?

....

e)   Sometimes fatty material can build up in the arteries leading to an organ. This build up can eventually cause a blockage. State **two** substances that will not reach the cells of the organ in the event of such a blockage.

1. ....   2. ....

Breathing

Q1   Dr Baker uses a **peak flow meter** to assess whether a patient is asthmatic.
The patient is asked to breathe out hard into the equipment.

a)   Fill in the blanks in the passage below to show what happens when the patient breathes out.

increase	thorax	decreases	intercostal	diaphragm	relax

When the patient breathes out, a muscle below the chest called the ....

relaxes and moves up. This .... the volume of the thorax, causing the

pressure in the lungs to ...., forcing air out of the lungs. The

.... muscles (the muscles between the ribs) also ....

when breathing out.

b)   Number the following structures (1-6) in order to show the route that oxygen takes when
the patient breaths out into the peak flow meter. The first one has been done for you.

☐ bronchiole   [1] alveolus   ☐ trachea

☐ bronchus   ☐ peak flow meter   ☐ mouth cavity

c)   During gaseous exchange where do the gases O_2 and CO_2 move from and to?

....

....

Q2   Many people suffer from problems with the **respiratory system**, so
it's important for **doctors** to learn about the structure of the thorax.

Draw lines to match the letters from the diagram with
their correct names.

| A |
| B |
| C |
| D |
| E |
| F |

diaphragm muscle

alveoli

intercostal muscle

bronchus

trachea

bronchiole

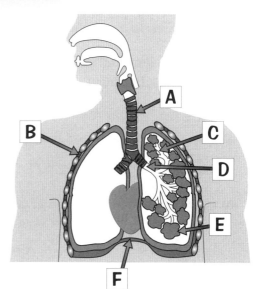

Top Tips: It's important to remember that air moves in and out of the lungs, not because
it just feels like it, but because of the change in pressure within the thorax. By relaxing and
contracting the intercostal muscles and the diaphragm, a difference in pressure is created.

8

The Nervous System

Q1 Sam was sitting at his desk in his bedroom when he suddenly heard a **loud bang** coming from downstairs. It caused him to jump up from his chair and his heart rate increased.

   a) Tick the boxes to show whether these statements are **true** or **false**.

                                                                                True False

     i) Sam detected the stimulus using light receptors.

     ii) The loud bang was the stimulus.

     iii) Sam detected the stimulus using a sense organ.

     iv) The sound receptors in Sam's ears generated an electrical impulse.

     v) Sam's heart beat was the stimulus.

   b) Give **two** responses caused by the loud bang.

     1. ....

     2. ....

Q2 Jamie was cooking his mum some tea when he accidentally picked up a **hot** saucepan. Jamie **instantly** dropped the pan back onto the hob.

   a) Put numbers in the boxes so that the following statements are in the correct order to describe how Jamie's nervous system responded to him picking up the hot pan.

     [ ] Some of the muscles in Jamie's hand contract causing him to drop the pan.

     [1] Temperature receptors in Jamie's hand detect the increase in temperature.

     [ ] Impulses travel along a motor neurone.

     [ ] Impulses travel along a sensory neurone.

     [ ] The information is processed by the spinal cord.

   b) The muscles in Jamie's hand are an example of one type of effector. There are two types of **effectors** — two different ways the body can respond to a stimulus.

     i) Name the other type of effector.

     ....

     ii) How does this type of effector bring about a response in the body?

     ....

The Nervous System

Q3   John has suffered **damage** to his **spinal cord**. His doctor says it has been completely severed. The diagram shows the position of the damage.

a)   What is the function of the spinal cord?

....

....

b)   Suggest **how** the injury will affect John's movements.

....

....

c)   Give a reason **why** the injury will affect John's movements.

....

....

....

spinal cord
damaged
at this point

d)   John's doctor decides to test his nerves by pressing a blunt needle against his skin in different places.

i)   What types of receptors does John's skin contain?

....

ii)   Tick the boxes to show if John is able to feel the needle on his:

	Yes	No
neck	☐	☐
hand	☐	☐
knee	☐	☐

e)   When the needle is pressed against John's skin, information is transmitted from one neurone to another.

i)   What name is given to the gap between two neurones? ....

ii)   Describe how electrical impulses cross this gap.

....

....

Top Tips: So that's the nervous system — I'm sure it wasn't that painful. Not as painful as being poked in the eye with a cactus, I bet. Hmm... I wonder what type of receptors would be involved during a round of eye poking. I imagine the response would probably be anger.

Maintaining Body Temperature

Q1 Yolanda and Subarna are on holiday in **Egypt**, where the daytime **temperature** can get uncomfortably **high**.

a) Yolanda and Subarna notice that they are sweating more than usual. They are told that the blood vessels close to the surface of their skin get bigger in diameter in the heat.

Tick the boxes to show whether these statements are **true** or **false**.

                                                                            True   False

i) When water in sweat evaporates, it carries heat away with it. ☐ ☐

ii) More heat is lost to the surroundings when blood vessels close to the skin's surface are smaller in diameter. ☐ ☐

iii) Sweating causes your body to retain heat. ☐ ☐

b) Which part of the body identifies an increase in the temperature of the blood?

....

Q2 A rescue team discovered an injured climber on a mountain ledge. The rescue team were concerned that the mountaineer was suffering from hypothermia — a **dangerously low body temperature**.

a) When you are cold, your blood vessels change in order to help maintain body temperature. Circle the correct words in the passage below to describe how.

> When you are too cold, blood vessels close to the skin's surface get smaller / larger in diameter. This means that more / less blood gets to the surface of the skin. This stops the blood from losing / gaining its heat to the surroundings.

b) The rescue team carried out first aid that involved the following procedures. In each case, explain how the procedure would reduce the risk of hypothermia.

i) They put the mountaineer in an insulating blanket.

....

ii) Wet clothing cools the body in the same way that sweat does. Suggest why the rescue team removed the mountaineer's wet clothing and replaced it with dry clothing.

....

Hormones and Blood Sugar

Q1 Beverley is late for her maths exam. She has just got off her bus and is running to her school. Beverley's body is responding to both her **hormonal system** and her **nervous system**.

a) Tick the boxes to show whether these statements are **true** or **false**.

	True	False
i) The nervous system can create an immediate reaction.	☐	☐
ii) Nervous responses act for a longer time than hormonal responses.	☐	☐
iii) Hormones are chemical signals.	☐	☐
iv) Nerve impulses act on more precise areas than hormones.	☐	☐
v) Hormones generate a signal as a result of a stimulus. The nervous system does not.	☐	☐

> As she is running to school, Beverley must cross a pedestrian crossing and has to wait for the lights to turn green. Another student is waiting beside her, and he is eating a hamburger rather noisily. It reminds Beverley that she hasn't eaten breakfast that morning. When she eventually arrives at the exam room, she is exhausted and hungry.

b) Give two types of stimuli that Beverley experienced on her travels to school.

1. ....

2. ....

c) Name two sense organs that Beverley used to detect the stimuli.

1. .... 2. ....

Q2 Jack has recently been diagnosed with gigantism — a condition caused by having too much growth hormone. His doctor is explaining how **hormones function**.

glands	target	blood	chemicals

Hormones are .... that are produced

in .... They are released directly into

the .... They travel all over the

body but only affect .... cells.

You've got too much growth hormone.

Hormones and Blood Sugar

Q3 A research scientist is investigating the effect of diet on blood glucose levels. The graph below shows the levels of **glucose** in the blood for two different people after they had both consumed exactly the same type of meal.

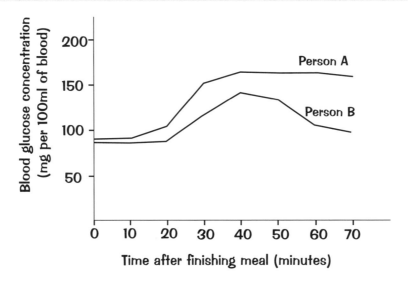

a) Insulin controls the levels of glucose in the blood. Where in the body is insulin produced?

....

b) When did the blood sugar level of person B start to decrease?

....

c) Number the stages (1-4) to show one way in which blood sugar levels decrease.

☐ The pancreas releases insulin.

☐ A rise in glucose level detected by pancreas.

☐ Glucose is stored as glycogen.

☐ Insulin causes the liver to take up glucose from blood.

d) Why was it important to ensure that both people in this experiment consumed the same meal before measurements of blood sugar were taken?

....

....

Top Tips: It's important to know about hormones, especially insulin. Comparing the hormonal system and the nervous system is pretty useful as it'll help you remember the similarities and differences between the two. Now where's those biscuits... I feel my blood sugar dropping.

Genes and Chromosomes

Q1 **Geneticists** study the **genes** and **chromosomes** inside cells, as well as the way in which different characteristics are **inherited**. By looking at cells, geneticists can sometimes identify abnormalities in the chromosomes.

a) Fill in the missing words in the following passage.

Short sections of chromosomes are called ....

There may be slightly different versions of genes carried on each

chromosome of a particular pair. These versions of genes are called

....

b) Arrange the following in order of size, giving the smallest first and the largest last:

gene   cell   chromosome   nucleus

....

Q2 During IVF treatment, embryos are checked for **abnormalities** in the **chromosomes**. A clinical molecular geneticist extracts **one cell** to study. The embryo is shown below.

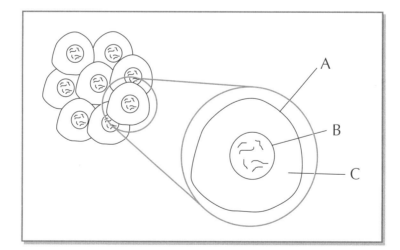

a) Which part of the cell, **A**, **B**, or **C**, contains the chromosomes? ....

b) What is the name for this part of a cell? ....

c) Each chromosome contains many genes. What do genes control?

....

Top Tips: Make sure that you properly understand this stuff because it's really important in the rest of the section. Unless it's in your genes that you're a genius, then you'd better get learning.

Variation in Plants and Animals

Q1   Mr Brown has **red hair** and Mrs Brown has **black hair**. They have four children.

a)   Fill in the blanks in the passage to explain why each child will have different characteristics.

genes   sexual   reproduction   genetic

> Some differences in the characteristics of the Brown's children are due to
>
> .... causes. During ....,
>
> some of Mr Brown's .... are grouped with some of Mrs Brown's
>
> .... and so the child will receive a mixture of these.

b)   Tick the boxes to show whether the following statements
about Mr and Mrs Brown's children are **true** or **false**.

	True	False
i) The children will share some characteristics with Mr and Mrs Brown.	☐	☐
ii) The children will resemble Mr and Mrs Brown because they have exactly the same genes.	☐	☐
iii) The children will each have some chromosomes from Mr Brown and some from Mrs Brown.	☐	☐

Here, these jeans might help your big nose...

Q2   Sam, Bob and Alfie are brothers. Sam and Bob are both
5 years old and are **identical twins**. Alfie is 8 years old.

a)   Sam **weighs more** than Bob. Is this difference due to their
genes or their environment? Give a reason for your answer.

....

....

Don't forget they're identical twins

b)   Suggest **two** of Alfie's characteristics that are likely to be determined by a
combination of his genes and his environment.

1. ....

2. ....

c)   Explain why Alfie will share **fewer** characteristics with Sam than Bob shares with Sam.

....

....

....

Variation in Plants and Animals

Q3   Al and Mo are brother and sister. The diagram below shows some of their **characteristics**.

Al   **Mo**

brown hair   blonde hair

scar from   brown eyes   blue eyes
rugby accident

speaks English
and French

speaks English   star tattoo

blood group A   blood group B

a)   Draw lines to connect the boxes to show which of Al and Mo's characteristics are **genetically** determined and which are **environmentally** determined.

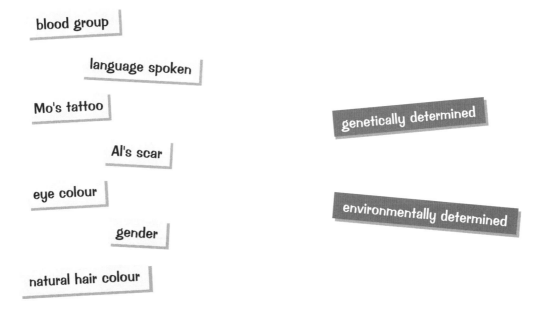

blood group

language spoken

Mo's tattoo

genetically determined

Al's scar

eye colour

environmentally determined

gender

natural hair colour

b)   Suggest **two** factors that can cause genetic variation.

1. ....

2. ....

c)   Al and Mo have different shaped ear lobes. Ear lobe shape is controlled by one gene.
Why do Al and Mo have different shaped ear lobes?

....

....

Inherited Characteristics

Q1 Sally is a **geneticist**. She studies people's **genes** to help her understand the way certain characteristics are **inherited** from one generation to the next.

Tick the boxes to show whether the following statements are **true** or **false**.

True False

a) Someone with one recessive allele will not display the characteristic of that allele. ☐ ☐

b) A single dominant allele in a cell is never sufficient for the allele's characteristic to be displayed. ☐ ☐

c) Genes are parts of chromosomes, which are found in the nucleus of a cell. ☐ ☐

d) A child of two parents who are carriers for a recessive allele will definitely display the recessive characteristic. ☐ ☐

These were once your great-great-great grandfather's.

Q2 David and Jane have three children called James, Ruth and Jenny. James was born with **cystic fibrosis** but is the only sufferer in his family.

a) **F** is the normal allele and **f** is the **recessive**, faulty allele that causes cystic fibrosis. What combination of alleles does James have?

....

b) **i)** What combination of alleles must David and Jane have? Circle the correct answer.

FF and Ff   **Ff and Ff**   **FF and FF**   **ff and ff**   **ff and Ff**

ii) Give a reason for your answer.

....

....

c) Jenny grew up to marry Michael. Michael has no history of cystic fibrosis in his family. Tick the answer that correctly describes the chance of them having a child with cystic fibrosis.

☐ **Impossible — neither Jenny nor Michael is a sufferer.**

☐ **Possible — they could both be carriers of the allele that causes cystic fibrosis.**

☐ **Possible — Jenny must be a carrier, so it doesn't matter what alleles Michael has.**

Top Tips: Don't worry if the exam questions aren't about genetic disorders. They could ask you about the inheritance of eye colour or hair colour instead, but it works just like the stuff on these pages — the same rules apply.

Inherited Characteristics

Q3 **Huntington's disease** is a **genetic disorder** that usually develops later in life, after people have had children. The disorder is controlled by a dominant allele. Tara's family has a history of Huntington's disease, as shown in the family tree diagram.

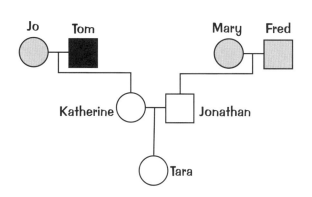

male with no symptoms of Huntington's disease

female with no symptoms of Huntington's disease

male sufferer of Huntington's disease

female sufferer of Huntington's disease

male without allele for Huntington's disease

female without allele for Huntington's disease

a) **i)** Circle the correct word(s) to complete the following sentence about Tara's chance of developing Huntington's disease.

Tara will **definitely** / **possibly** / **definitely not** develop Huntington's disease.

ii) Give a reason for your answer.

....

....

b) **i)** Which of Tara's parents **could** develop Huntington's disease? Circle the correct answer.

Tara's mum (Katherine)   **Tara's dad (Jonathan)**

ii) Give a reason for your answer.

....

....

Q4 A genetic counsellor is explaining **inheritance** to a couple who are worried about passing on two different **genetic disorders**, sickle-cell anaemia and Marfan syndrome, to offspring they might have.

Complete the table by circling the correct answers to show which of the statements refer to sickle-cell anaemia and which refer to Marfan syndrome. Two answers have already been completed for you.

Don't worry if you haven't heard of these disorders. You can work out the answers using your knowledge of dominant and recessive alleles.

	Sickle-cell anaemia	Marfan syndrome
Controlled by a recessive allele	yes / no	yes / no
Controlled by a dominant allele	yes / no	yes / no
Can be inherited from just one parent	yes / no	yes / no
Two copies of the faulty allele are needed for the disease to occur	yes / no	yes / no

Health & Medicine

18

Treating Genetic Disorders

Q1   **Gene therapy** is an experimental treatment for genetic disorders, which involves inserting a working version of a faulty gene into a patient's cells.

A scientist is conducting research into two gene therapy techniques used to treat cystic fibrosis. He treats 100 people with cystic fibrosis using Technique 1 and another 100 with Technique 2. He assesses their side effects and symptoms over 6 months. His results are shown in the table.

Technique	% suffering side effects	% symptom-free for 2 months	% symptom-free for 6 months	cost per patient
1	65	76	61	2500
2	32	56	42	1600

a)   How many people were symptom-free after six months following Technique 1?

....

b)   How many more people were symptom-free after two months following Technique 1 than following Technique 2?

....

c)   How many people suffered side effects following Technique 2? Circle the correct answer.

  76   56   32   65

d)   Which technique produced the longest lasting results?

....

e)   Why might people decide against this technique even though it produced the longest lasting results in this study?

....

f)   Which technique might a hospital prefer to provide to its patients? Explain your answer.

....

....

Top Tips: Don't panic if you're faced with an exam question about some treatment that you've never even heard of before. Just keep cool — you won't be expected to know the details. As long as you can read data from graphs and tables, you'll be absolutely fine.

Section 2.2 — Genetics   _Health & Medicine_

Treating Genetic Disorders

Q2 The **Human Genome Project** involved scientists finding the location of **genes** on all **human chromosomes**. Humans have 23 pairs of chromosomes in their body cells, and around **25 000** different kinds of genes spread between them. The graph below shows the **number** of genes associated with **disease** discovered since the start of the Human Genome Project.

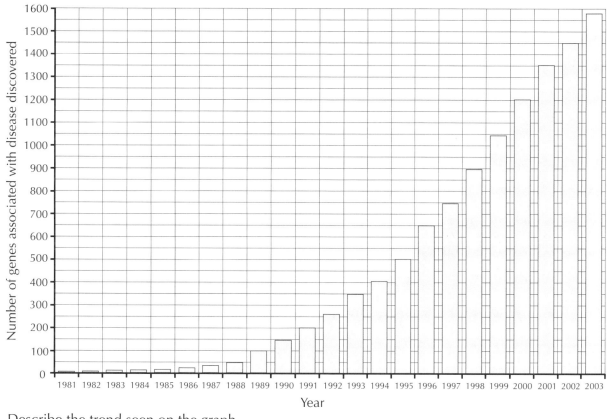

a) Describe the trend seen on the graph.

....

b) How many genes associated with disease had been discovered by 1996?

....

c) How long did it take scientists to discover 1200 genes?

....

d) Tick the boxes next to statements that describe ways that the human genome project could make a difference to the way genetic disorders are treated.

☐ It could make it easier to diagnose genetic disorders.

☐ Vaccines can be developed.

☐ New genes can be developed.

☐ Faulty genes responsible for genetic disorders may be identified.

Microorganisms and Disease

Q1 After eating some **leftovers** that weren't **reheated properly** Ashley has been suffering from **food poisoning**.

a) Food poisoning can be caused by pathogens. What are pathogens?

....

b) Name the two types of microorganisms below.

A. ....   B. ....

c) Tick the boxes to show whether the following statements are true or false.

	True	False
i) All bacteria cause disease	☐	☐
ii) Bacteria don't have a nucleus	☐	☐
iii) Bacteria are not living	☐	☐

d) Give two ways that bacteria can make you feel ill.

1. ....   2. ....

Q2 Annie is recovering from **measles** — a disease caused by a **virus**. Number the statements so that they are in the correct order to show how the measles virus made Annie feel **ill**.

☐ The invaded cells burst, releasing more measles viruses.

☐ The measles virus uses Annie's cells to replicate and produce more viruses.

☐ The measles virus invades Annie's cells.

☐ The new measles viruses go on to invade more of Annie's cells.

Q3 Michael is a specialist in **infectious diseases**. He studies diseases caused by microorganisms.

Name three diseases, not already mentioned on this page, that are caused by microorganisms.

1. ....   2. ....

3. ....

Microorganisms and Disease

Q4 John is a **health inspector**. He ensures that places serving food to the public keep a certain **standard of hygiene**.

a) Explain why John should examine the following things:

i) Food

....

ii) Water

....

iii) Surfaces

....

b) When John was inspecting a pub kitchen he noticed the chopping board that is used to prepare raw chicken is also used to prepare salad. Why could this be dangerous?

....

....

Q5 Jackie is an **epidemiologist**, which means she studies outbreaks of disease. Disease can spread by unhygienic conditions or by contact with an infected person.

a) Draw lines to match the descriptions of the diseases with how they are spread.

Cholera is found in raw sewage

contact with infected people.

Flu is found in droplets in the air breathed out by an infected person

unhygienic conditions.

b) Explain why you are more likely to catch flu when sitting next to someone infected with flu on a long-haul flight than you would be if you passed the same person in the street.

....

....

Top Tips: If you're a microorganism then the human body probably seems like luxury. It provides an excellent environment for microorganisms to grow. The more microorganisms that manage to get into the luxury hotel that is your body, the more likely you are to get the disease.

Reducing the Spread of Disease

Q1   Froggart's Pharmaceuticals have developed a new **antiseptic** called
"Germ-no-more" that is about to hit the shops and hospitals.

a)   Fill in the gaps in the sentences below to show what might be on the label of Germ-no-more.

skin	microorganisms	cuts	chemical

An antiseptic is a .... that can be used on

the .... to clean ....

Antiseptics kill some ....

b)   Frank is a medical sales rep who is trying to sell Germ-no-more to a hospital.
What could Frank suggest they use Germ-no-more for?

....

Q2   Metal **surgical equipment** is often **sterilised** using an autoclave. This uses very high **temperatures**.

a)   Why does surgical equipment have to be sterilised?

....

b)   How does the autoclave sterilise surgical equipment?

....

c)   What might be used to sterilise **plastic** surgical equipment?

....

Q3   Hygiene in **hospitals** is extremely important to **reduce** the spread of diseases such as MRSA.

a)   Explain how using disinfectants helps to prevent the spread of disease in hospitals.

....

....

b)   Why don't nurses use disinfectant to clean their hands?

....

c)   What could nurses use instead of disinfectant to clean their hands?

....

Reducing the Spread of Disease

Q4   Doctors should **wash their hands** before and after examining
a patient and **wear gloves** when taking blood samples.

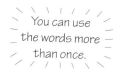
You can use the words more than once.

Use the words below to complete the paragraph about why they should do this.

mouth	microorganisms	nose	cells
patient	disease	eyes	hospital

Hand-washing reduces the risk of the doctors transferring ....

from patients to their ...., ... and ....

These parts of the body are where .... could enter and cause

.... It also stops them being transferred from doctor to patient and from

one .... to another. Wearing gloves will stop .... in the

patient's blood getting into any cuts the doctor may have.

Q5   When cooking **chicken** it is important to take a number
of **precautions** to prevent **food poisoning**. Complete the
table below to show what precautions you would take
and why they are necessary (some have been done for you).

Precaution	Why it is necessary
	Stops pathogens from your hands getting on the chicken.
The chicken is cooked thoroughly.	
	Stops pathogens from the raw chicken being transferred to your body or other food.
Disinfect the work top.	

Top Tips: Make sure you know all the different ways we can reduce the chance of being
exposed to pathogens. You should be doing some of these every day anyway, like practising good
personal hygiene. I doubt you get the opportunity to sterilise surgical equipment very often though.

The Body's Defence Systems

Q1 Sally is a **medical student** studying the ways that the body can **prevent** microorganisms entering.

a) Complete the passage using some of the words given in the box.

platelets	cells	clot	microorganisms	antibodies

The skin acts as a barrier to infection. If the skin is broken, e.g. if it is cut,

.... can get into the body. ..../

which are small fragments of ...., help the blood

...................................., which seals the wound and prevents infection.

b) Give two features, apart from skin, that can act as a barrier against pathogens.

1. ....

2. ....

Q2 Sophie is an **immunologist**. She studies how the body destroys different pathogens that enter it.

a) Circle the correct word(s) in each pair to complete each sentence below.

   i) The **circulatory / immune** system attacks microorganisms in the body.

   ii) The **white blood cells / platelets** in the body attack microorganisms.

b) Number the following sentences in the correct order to show how the body can attack an invading pathogen.

☐ The antibodies lock on to the antigens so that the pathogens can be killed by other white blood cells.

☐ The white blood cells recognise a foreign antigen.

☐ White blood cells produce antibodies specific to the antigens of the pathogen.

☐ If the person is infected with the same pathogen again, the white blood cells will produce antibodies very quickly to prevent the person from getting ill.

c) HIV attacks white blood cells. Suggest how this could affect people with HIV?

....

....

Having fewer white blood cells reduces the ability of the immune system.

Vaccination

Q1 Melissa has just had a baby called Josie. The doctor has advised her that Josie should be **vaccinated** against certain diseases.

a) Give **three** diseases that the Doctor might suggest Josie is vaccinated against.

1. ....

2. ....

3. ....

b) Melissa wants to know **why** the vaccines are necessary.
Fill in the gaps in the paragraph below using words from the box.

microorganism	white blood cells	vaccinated
antibodies	ill	immune

In the time it takes for the .... to make

.... some microorganisms can make you

very .... You can be ....

against some diseases so that you become ....

to that disease even though you've never actually encountered the live

....

c) Suggest what the doctor might say about the **risk** involved in giving Josie a vaccine.

....

....

....

d) Tick the boxes next to statements that are **advantages** of vaccination.

☐ If a high percentage of people are vaccinated against a disease, fewer unvaccinated people will catch it because there are fewer people with the disease to catch it from.

☐ Trained health workers are needed to administer vaccines.

☐ The fewer people that get ill, the lower the cost of treatment to hospitals.

Top Tips: Vaccinations are pretty brilliant really. You get given a few injections when you're young and it stops you getting all sorts of horrible diseases — diptheria, tetanus, rubella, polio, tuberculosis... Some diseases have almost disappeared now that loads of us are vaccinated.

Vaccination

Q? Scientists developed a new **vaccine** against **virus Z**. **Twenty people** took part in a **trial** of the vaccine. The results of the trial are shown in the table.

Number of people who became immune to virus Z.	18
Number of people who contracted the illness the next year.	1
Number of people who suffered side-effects.	7

a) Give **two** disadvantages of the new vaccine.

1. ....

2. ....

b) Give one advantage of having a vaccine against virus Z.

....

c) What percentage of participants became immune to the virus?

....

d) Scientists have studied the action of drugs used to treat infectious diseases.
They recommend that patients suffering from virus Z are **not** given antibiotics.

Why is this?

....

e) The following statements describe how vaccine Z works but they are in the wrong order.
Put numbers in the boxes to show the correct order.

☐ The inactive virus Z microorganisms carry antigens so the white blood cells make antibodies against them.

☐ Antibodies are made very quickly and the virus Z microorganisms are killed before they have a chance to make you ill.

☐ If virus Z enters the body again, the white blood cells recognise it straight away.

☐ Inactive virus Z is injected into the body.

Vaccination

Q3 The table shows the number of **cases** of **Disease X** reported in a country between 1982-2002. The graph shows the **uptake of the vaccine** used to prevent disease X.

a) Plot a graph of the data displayed in the table on the axis below.

Year	Number of cases
1982	7600
1986	7500
1990	7200
1994	6650
1998	6100
2002	5100

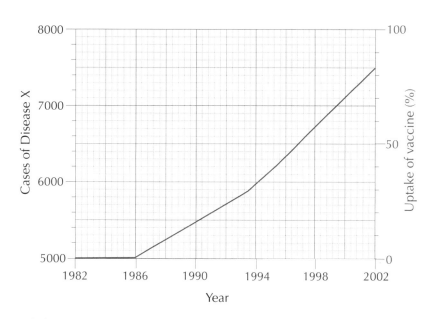

b) Describe and explain the trend shown on the graph between 1982 and 2002.

....

....

....

c) Which year was the vaccine introduced? ....

d) How many cases of Disease X were there in 1996? ....

e) The bar chart show the number of cases of Disease X in different areas of the country in 2005.

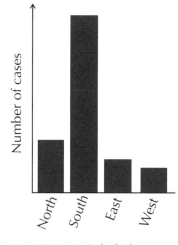

   i) In which area are most cases of Disease X found?

   ....

   ii) Suggest a reason why this area has the highest number of cases.

   ....

   ....

   ....

Think about what conditions increase the spread of disease.

Effects of Radiation on the Body

Q1   Pete is a technician who works in a hospital **radiography** department. Because he works with **radiation**, it is important that he understands what it is and how to work with it **safely**.

a)   Name the **three** main types of nuclear radiation.

1. ....

2. ....

3. ....

b)   Fill in the gaps below to show how radiation can harm living organisms.

molecules	ionisation	cells
Nuclear radiation causes .... This can damage or destroy .... by bashing into .... inside them.		

c)   Tick the boxes to show whether the statements are **true** or **false**.

	True	False
i) Pete should wear a mask when handling material that produces alpha radiation.	☐	☐
ii) Pete can safely store a source of beta radiation in an aluminium box.	☐	☐
iii) If Pete is exposed to an external source of gamma radiation it will cause more damage to his cells than a source of alpha radiation.	☐	☐
iv) Even though alpha particles can't pass through your skin into your body, Pete should wear gloves when handling alpha sources to prevent possible contamination with his mouth later on.	☐	☐

d)   Explain how being exposed to radiation can lead to **cancer**.

....

....

e)   What other illness can radiation exposure cause?

....

Medical Uses of Radiation

Q1 Ranjit is a **radiographer** who takes **X-rays** of people to see if they have any broken bones. When she takes X-rays of people she wears a **lead apron**.

a) Why does Ranjit need to wear a lead apron?

....

b) What other precautions could Ranjit take?

....

c) On the right is an X-ray photograph of a hand.

i) Label with an X on the diagram where fewer X-rays have passed through the person's body on to the photographic plate.

ii) Why can you see **bone** but not **flesh** in the X-ray?

....

....

iii) What other material would show up on an X-ray?

....

Only dense materials show up.

Q2 Julia has **breast cancer** and is being treated with **radiotherapy** by her doctors.

a) What type of radiation will Julia be treated with?

....

b) Fill in the gaps in the sentences below to explain how Julia's treatment works.

normal	dosage	kill	cells
X	gamma		carefully

.... rays are used to .... the cancerous

.... The right .... is directed

.... to avoid damaging .... cells.

c) Explain why Julia might suffer side effects from this treatment.

....

Healthy Diet

Q1   It's important to eat the **right amount of food** for your body size and level of activity, and it's also important to eat the right balance of foods.

Draw lines to match each food group to its main use in the body.

Vitamins and minerals

Fibre

Carbohydrates and fats

Protein

keeps everything moving through the digestive system

provide energy and insulation

growth, cell repair and replacement

keep the skin, blood and bones healthy

Q2   Steven is a **dietician**. He gives advice to people about how to eat a **healthy balanced diet**.

a)   Complete the table below to show which of the foods in the box are healthy and which are unhealthy when eaten in large amounts.

| salt | fresh fruit | sugar | fresh vegetables | saturated fat |

Generally healthy foods	**Generally unhealthy foods if eaten in excess**

b)   When giving advice Steven explains that the generally unhealthy food should still be eaten in small amounts. Why is this?

....

c)   Explain why it's important to eat a mixture of different fruit and veg.

....

....

Healthy Diet

Q3 Below is a food label for a **350 g** packet of a **curry ready meal** showing its nutritional content and the recommended daily amounts of nutrients for an average adult.

Typical values		per 100g	RDA
Energy	KJ	610	8400
	KCal	145	2000
Protein		10.6 g	45 g
Carbohydrate		4.7 g	230 g
Fat		9.5 g	70 g
of which saturates:		1.2 g	20 g
Salt		0.8 g	6 g

Don't forget that the label only gives you the amount of nutrients per 100 g, not for the whole meal.

a) How much fat does the **whole pack** contain?

....

b) What percentage of an adult's recommended daily amount of fat does this curry provide?

....

c) Eating an excess of fat can increase the risk of developing certain diseases.
Name one of these diseases.

....

d) What percentage of an adult's recommended daily amount of protein does this curry provide?

....

e) How much salt does the whole pack contain? Circle the correct answer.

   0.2 g   0.8 g   2.8 g   8.0 g

f) What percentage of an adult's recommended daily amount of salt does this curry provide?

....

> **Top Tips:** Just like riding a unicycle the key to a healthy diet is all about balance. Make sure you get enough of the healthy foods (like fresh fruit and veg) and not too much of the unhealthy stuff (like saturated fat, salt and sugar). And remember, always wear knee pads and a helmet.

Use of Drugs to Treat Disease

Q1   Mohan is a **pharmacist.** He dispenses drugs, e.g. antibiotics, to people who are unwell.

a)   What are antibiotics?

....

b)   Fill in the missing gaps below using words from the box.

antibiotics	body	aspirin	disease	dangerous

Drugs are chemicals that affect the way the .... works. Drugs are

.... if misused. Some drugs are used to treat ....,

for example .... (e.g. penicillin) and anti-inflammatories (e.g.

................................). Mohan can sell certain drugs over the counter, but other

drugs need to be prescribed by a doctor.

c)   Draw lines to match up the types of drugs with their function.

antivirals

painkillers

antibiotics

cold remedies

only relieve the symptoms of disease

target the cause of disease
(the pathogens)

Q2   Jo has a bad cold. Jo's brother had a **bacterial infection** and is still taking some **antibiotics** even though he is feeling much better. Seeing how quickly her brother's antibiotics worked, Jo goes to her local doctor to get some.

a)   Give one reason why the doctor should not give Jo antibiotics.

....

b)   What could the pharmacist give Jo to make her feel better?

....

c)   Why is it important that Jo's brother finishes his course of antibiotics even though he feels better?

....

....

Use of Drugs to Treat Disease

Q3 Melissa is a research scientist for a pharmaceutical company. She is currently researching a new **antibiotic** that the pharmaceutical company thinks could be used to kill the bacteria **MRSA**. Melissa wanted to compare the new antibiotic with some other antibiotics that were being developed. She placed some MRSA bacteria on a sterile agar plate. She then placed six discs of filter paper on the surface of the plate. Five discs had been soaked in different antibiotics and one was soaked in distilled water. The **clear zones** show where the bacteria have not grown.

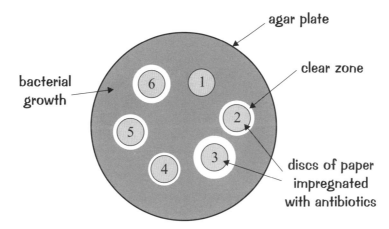

a) **i)** What **safety precautions** should Melissa take when carrying out this experiment?

....

ii) Why does she need to take these precautions?

....

b) **i)** Which disc do you think was soaked in **water**? How can you tell?

....

ii) Why do you think it was necessary to include this disc?

....

c) Why do you think it was important that Melissa used a **sterile** agar plate?

....

d) Disc number **6** was soaked in the new antibiotic.
How does the new antibiotic compare with the others?

....

....

e) Once Melissa has finished recording her results, the agar plate has to be incinerated (burnt). Why is it necessary to incinerate the agar plate?

....

Testing New Medical Drugs

Q1 Ushma is an **animal technician** who works for a pharmaceutical company.
She is involved in **testing new medicines** that are being developed by the company.

a) Why is it necessary for drugs to be tested before they can be sold and used by the public?

....

b) Number the following in the correct order to show the usual
development and testing process for new drugs.

☐ Live animals

☐ Human volunteers

☐ Computer models

☐ Human tissue

c) Explain why computer models are often used when developing drugs.

....

....

d) Tick the boxes to show whether the statements are **true** or **false**.

True   False

i) Human tissue can be used to test the effect of the drug on
a whole body system.   ☐   ☐

ii) In the UK, new drugs must be tested on two different live mammals.   ☐   ☐

iii) A placebo contains the new medicine being tested.   ☐   ☐

e) Use the words in the box to fill in the gaps in the paragraph about clinical trials below.

side effects	small	healthy	large	control	placebo	animals

A clinical trial takes place after the drug has been tested on .... In the first

stage the drug is tested on .... human volunteers, to determine if the drug has

any .... If the results from the first stage are good, the drug is then tested on

a .... number of patients and then a .... number of patients.

At each stage of the clinical trial a .... group is given a dummy that does not

contain the active drug being tested. This dummy is called a ....

Top Tips: It takes years for a drug to reach the general public. It has to go through loads
of different stages to make sure it is effective and has no serious side effects. Some of these stages
of drug development are pretty controversial, as you'll see on the next page...

Testing New Medical Drugs

Q2   Read the extract below and answer the following questions.

> Animal rights campaigners gathered in Corel Square today to demonstrate against the opening of Froggarts' new animal testing laboratory. This lab carries out the final tests of new drugs on animals to make sure they're safe before they're given to humans.
>
> I interviewed several of the animal rights campaigners, who made their grievances with the company very clear, saying, "Animals are so different from humans that testing on them is pointless", "Why should animals suffer for our benefit?" and "Animal testing shouldn't be used because it has failed to highlight the harmful side effects of some drugs".
>
> Despite these arguments, voiced by many pressure groups, the law states that 'finished' drugs must be tested on animals before they can be regarded as suitable for human trials.
>
> The head of scientific research at Froggarts pointed out that, "We share over 90% of our DNA with other primates and many other animals have very similar organs to our own, making them good models of the human body". However, he admitted that, "an extremely small number of side effects that humans experience cannot be detected in other organisms, but animal testing is still the safest way to make sure a drug isn't harmful to humans".
>
> In 2005, 395 000 animals were used for safety experiments in the UK. Of these animals, 73% were used for testing the safety of drugs. There are several laws in place to ensure that any pain caused by testing is kept to a minimum. These laws make UK testing regulations amongst the strictest in the world.
>
> The benefits of testing on animals are clear when you consider the millions of people whose lives have been improved by these drugs. For example, approximately 35 000 people are treated for breast cancer every year with drugs that have been tested on animals.
>
> Testing drugs on animals has been a highly controversial issue for decades. Without a realistic alternative in view, it will remain so for the foreseeable future.

a)   How many animals were used for safety experiments in 2005?

....

b)   Give two reasons why the animal rights campaigners object to testing new medicines on live animals.

....

....

c)   Explain why the head of scientific research at Froggart's still thinks that animals are good models to show how a new drug may work in humans.

....

....

Recreational Drugs

Q1   Legal and illegal drugs can be used **recreationally**.
There are many harmful effects of these drugs.

a)   Name **two** legal recreational drugs.

1. ....

2. ....

b)   Draw lines to link the drugs below to their correct descriptions.

Antidepressants   Medical drugs used as sedatives

Amphetamine   Stimulants designed to reduce depression

Nicotine   Stimulant drug — its common name is speed

Barbiturates   Addictive drug found in cigarettes

c)   Fill in the blanks in the paragraph using words from the box below.

kill	chemical	overdose
addictive	physical	withdrawal

Drugs change some of the .... processes in the body. Most drugs that are

used recreationally can be ...., meaning that the person can have a

.... need for the drug. If they don't have the drug they might get

.... symptoms. If too much of a drug is in your body it can cause an

.... and may .... you.

d)   The misuse of recreational drugs can have harmful physical and psychological effects.
Describe one harmful effect of each of the following drugs.

i)   Cocaine

....

ii) Stimulants

....

Recreational Drugs

Q2 Wayne is a regular user of **heroin**. Heroin has to be injected into the blood. Why shouldn't he **share needles** with other users?

Think about what blood could contain.

....

....

Q3 A **drug counsellor** is discussing the **effects of alcohol** with an addict.

a) Give **two** reasons why it is dangerous to drink and drive.

....

....

b) Drinking alcohol in excess can cause damage to the body. Fill in the blanks in the paragraph using words from the box below.

liver	inhibited	brain	dehydration

Drinking alcohol can make you feel less .... However, alcohol in excess can cause .... It can also damage brain cells, causing a noticeable drop in .... function. Too much alcohol can also cause severe damage to the ....

c) Outline the social problems that alcohol can cause.

....

....

....

Top Tips: Both legal and illegal drugs can have a major impact on your body. Drugs can also be addictive and cause antisocial behaviour, especially when used in excess. Alcohol's one of the most common legal drugs around but it still causes some really serious problems — so if you're going to use it, do it in moderation. And as for the illegal drugs, it's really not worth getting involved.

Recreational Drugs

Q4 The graphs below show the number of deaths due to **heart disease** and **lung cancer** for **smokers** and **non-smokers** from a study of a group of 100 000 men.

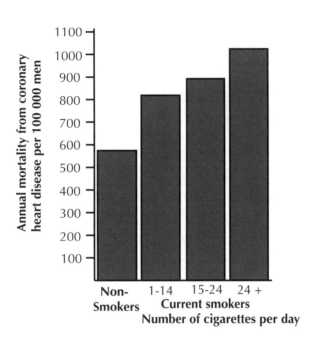

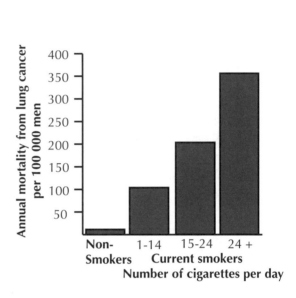

a) Approximately how many more deaths from coronary heart disease were there in smokers who smoke 1-14 cigarettes a day than in non-smokers?

.... per year per 100 000 men.

b) What is the difference between the number of lung cancer deaths in men smoking 15-24 cigarettes a day and men smoking more than 24 cigarettes a day? Circle the correct answer.

150

50

400

15

c) Does the bar chart show a **correlation** between smoking and heart disease? Explain your answer.

....

....

d) Explain why should you include as many people as possible in a study of the effects of smoking.

....

Think about reliability.

....

Recreational Drugs

e) Suggest another group of people that it would have been helpful to include in the study.
Give a reason for your answer.

....

Think about who wasn't tested in the study.

....

f) Circle the name of the chemicals that are present in tobacco smoke that can cause **cancer**.

emphysema   carcinogens   barbiturates   amphetamines

g) Which chemical in cigarettes makes smoking **addictive**?

....

h) Circle the correct word(s) in each pair to complete the paragraph
describing the effects of smoking on the **circulatory system**.

> Cigarettes contain carbon monoxide, which can combine with
>
> oxygen / haemoglobin in the red / white blood cells.   This means
>
> that the blood can carry less / more oxygen. Smoking
>
> also causes disease of the stomach / heart and blood vessels.
>
> This can lead to heart attacks / emphysema and cancer / strokes.

i) Explain how an unborn baby can be affected if a woman smokes when pregnant.

....

....

j) Smoking can cause respiratory diseases, e.g. lung cancer.
Name two other respiratory diseases that can be caused by smoking.

1. ....

2. ....

Top Tips: Smoking ain't big and it ain't clever. Amongst other things, it increases your chances of heart disease, there's evidence that links it to lung cancer and it's expensive. When I was young we just wasted out money on football stickers and I'm pretty sure they don't cause cancer.

Mixed Questions for Sections 2.1-2.3

Q1   Larry has made a **New Year's resolution** to become more **healthy**. He asks his **doctor** for advice. His doctor suggests he should give up smoking and gradually increase his level of exercise.

a)   i)   Suggest **one** reason why Larry might find it difficult to give up smoking.

....

ii)   Larry has had several **chest infections** in the last few months. His doctor says that this may be linked to **smoking**. Explain how smoking may have led to these chest infections.

....

....

b)   i)   Larry goes **jogging** with his friend Bill to improve his fitness. Whilst he is jogging, Larry starts sweating and his cheeks go red. Explain how these responses help cool Larry down.

....

....

....

ii)   After their run, Larry is hungry and wants to eat a chocolate bar, but Bill suggests he eats a banana instead. Which would be better for Larry's health? Give a reason for your answer.

....

iii)   Larry noticed that when he was jogging, his breathing rate increased. Complete the passage below to explain what happens as Larry breathes.   *Some words will be needed more than once.*

decreases	relax	increases	contract

When Larry breathes in, his intercostals and diaphragm .... and

his thorax volume .... This .... the pressure,

causing air to enter. When Larry breathes out, his intercostals and diaphragm

.... and his thorax volume ....

This .... the pressure, forcing air out.

Q2   **Emphysema** is a lung disorder that decreases the amount of **oxygen** passing from the **lungs** into the **bloodstream**.

a)   By which process does oxygen pass from the lungs into the blood? ....

b)   What causes this process to happen?

....

....

Mixed Questions for Sections 2.1-2.3

Q3 Marvin is designing a computer programme which models the way **neurones** send impulses to each other. He bases the programme on real animal cells.

a) The diagram below shows a typical animal cell.
Describe the function of each of the labelled parts.

i) nucleus ....

....

ii) cytoplasm ....

....

iii) cell membrane ....

b) Describe **two** specialisations of a neurone which make it different from the cell above, and explain how each specialisation helps its function.

1. ....

2. ....

c) Marvin's computer program contains model neurones that **detect stimuli**.

i) What are the biological equivalents of these cells called? ....

ii) Give **two** examples of this type of cell. ....

Q4 James is feeling **ill** and thinks that he must have an **infection**. He goes to see a doctor.

a) The doctor tells James that he has **influenza**, which is a viral infection.
Name **two** other illnesses caused by viruses.

1. .... 2. ....

b) Give **two** ways that white blood cells respond to viruses and other pathogens entering the body.

1. ....

2. ....

c) How could James have reduced his chances of being infected with influenza?

....

d) Tick the boxes to show whether the following statements about viruses are **true** or **false**.

	True	False
i) Viruses are killed by antibiotics.	☐	☐
ii) Viruses usually damage body cells when they replicate.	☐	☐

Health & Medicine

Mixed Questions for Sections 2.1-2.3

Q5 Jane and Roy have three children — Chantelle, Emma and a **new-born** baby daughter called Shakira.

a) Jane and Roy are keen to protect Shakira from infections until her immune system is better developed. Suggest **two** things they can do to protect her from infection.

1. ....

2. ....

b) Chantelle and Emma are **identical twins**. Tick the correct boxes to show whether the statements below are true or false.

True   False

i) Jane and Roy are genetically identical. ☐ ☐

ii) Chantelle and Emma are genetically identical. ☐ ☐

iii) The twins will have some chromosomes from both of their parents. ☐ ☐

iv) The twins will have chromosomes only from their father Roy. ☐ ☐

c) Although Chantelle and Emma are identical twins, they do not look exactly the same. Explain why this is.

....

....

d) Jane and Roy are both carriers of the allele that causes **sickle-cell anaemia**, a disease that affects **red blood cells**. The allele (**a**) that causes the disease is recessive. Below is a genetic diagram showing the probability of Jane and Roy's children suffering from the disease.

Roy   Jane

Aa   Aa

A   a   A   a

AA   Aa   Aa   aa

The sickle-cell allele is recessive — those with only one copy will be carriers but will not suffer from the disease.

i) What chance does each child have of having the disorder?

....

ii) Give **one** way in which red blood cells are adapted for their function.

....

Mixed Questions for Sections 2.1-2.3

Q6 Jonathan works as a **radiotherapist** in a hospital.
He uses ionising **radiation** to treat cancer patients.

a) Draw lines to match the three main types of radiation to their description and their properties.

alpha particles	small, light and fast moving	weakly ionising
beta particles	high energy electromagnetic waves	quite ionising
gamma rays	big, heavy and slow moving	very ionising

b) In some cases treating cancer with radiotherapy is unsuccessful and patients require an operation. Complete the passage using words from the list to describe how radiation is used to sterilise surgical apparatus used in operations.

alpha	gamma	metal	plastic	kill	freezing	boiling

Doctors sometimes sterilise medical instruments using high doses of

.... rays. These rays .... all microbes. This is a

better method of sterilisation than .... because it doesn't involve

high temperatures. This means that heat-sensitive equipment, e.g. instruments made

of ...., can be sterilised without causing damage.

Q7 Doctors can try to prevent diseases by using **vaccinations**, as well as treating them with **drugs**.

a) Explain how vaccinations work to help prevent disease.

....

....

....

b) Medical drugs must be tested thoroughly before use. One stage of this involves testing using live animals. Give one argument **for** and one argument **against** testing drugs on animals.

For ....

....

Against ....

....

Mixed Questions for Sections 2.1-2.3

Q8   Ryan has **diabetes**. The specialist at his local hospital is explaining the role of insulin in the body. He tells Ryan that insulin is a **hormone** that controls blood sugar levels.

a)   Explain how **insulin** works to control blood sugar levels in the body.

....

....

b)   Hormones are chemical messengers that travel around the body in the blood.

   i)   Name **four** things that the blood contains and describe the function of each.

1. ....

2. ....

3. ....

4. ....

   ii)   The blood is pumped around the body by the heart in a double circulatory system. Explain what a double circulatory system is.

....

....

c)   **Nerves** also carry messages around the body, but they do this in a different way from hormones. Fill in the table to show how messages sent by nerves and hormones differ.

act on a very precise area   chemical signal   very fast message

electrical signal   act for a long time

act in a more general way   slower message   act for a short time

Nerves	Hormones

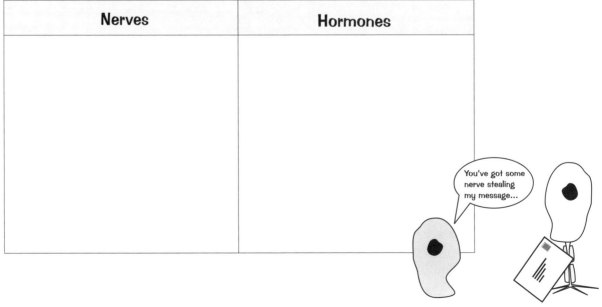

You've got some nerve stealing my message...

Health & Medicine

Specialised Plant Cells

Q1 Sheila is a **botanist** (a scientist who studies plants). She is looking at the roots of a plant under a **microscope**. She sees that the **roots** are covered in tiny **hairs**.

a) What is the purpose of root hair cells?

....

b) What feature of root hair cells makes them ideal for this purpose?

....

....

Q2 The diagram below shows a typical plant **leaf cell**.

a) Draw lines between the boxes to match each structure to its name and function. One has been done for you.

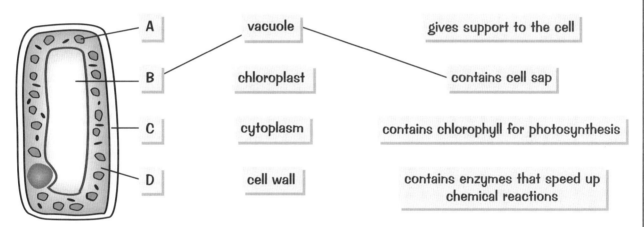

A	vacuole	gives support to the cell
B	chloroplast	contains cell sap
C	cytoplasm	contains chlorophyll for photosynthesis
D	cell wall	contains enzymes that speed up chemical reactions

b) Name **three** structures that are present in plant cells but not in animal cells.

....

Q3 Jasmine is a **research scientist** studying how leaf cells are specially adapted for photosynthesis. Complete the following passage about specialised leaf cells using words from the list below.

photosynthesis	surface area	stomata	light	many
respiration	chloroplasts	carbon dioxide	oxygen	palisade

Palisade leaf cells are specially adapted for .... Their tall,

thin shape means that .... can be placed close together

in the .... layer of the leaf. Each cell contains many

.... Their cylindrical shape also means that there's a

large .... for absorption of ....

What Plants Need

Q1   Dominic is an **agricultural consultant** who advises farmers on how to increase crop yield. He says that sunlight is very important because plants produce their own 'food' using **sunlight**.

   a)   What is the name of the process that plants use to produce their own food?

   ....

   b)   Write a word equation for this process.

   ....

Q2   Farmer Stubbs is learning about the things her crops need to **produce** their own **food**. Complete the passage below using words from the list.

chlorophyll	soil	oxygen	water	energy
green	carbon dioxide	light	chloroplasts	

.... enters leaves from the surrounding air. ....

is drawn up from the .... from the Sun

provides ...., which is absorbed by the ....

pigment called ...., found in ....

Q3   Leaves have some **special features** that make plants good at producing their own food.

   a)   Match each of the following features of a leaf with its purpose.

   | Leaves are thin and flat | to increase the chance of light hitting a chloroplast. |

   | Leaves have palisade cells near the surface | to allow movement of gases. |

   | Leaves have guard cells | to provide a large surface area to catch sunlight. |

   b)   The diagram below shows section through a leaf. Add labels to the diagram to show a guard cell and a palisade cell.

What Plants Need

Q4 Richard grows houseplants **commercially** for sale to garden centres. Over the years Richard has spent a lot of money building **glass houses** in which to grow his plants.

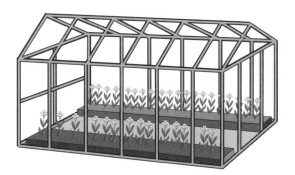

a) Richard **burns fuel** in his glass houses to increase the air temperature, making his plants grow faster.

   i) Why does increasing the air temperature make them grow faster?

     ....

     ....

   ii) In addition to heat, what does burning fuel produce?

     ....

   iii) Why does this other product help Richard's plants to grow faster?

     ....

     ....

b) Richard's glass houses also have **artificial lighting**.

   i) When would Richard use the artificial lighting?

     ....

   ii) What benefit does the artificial lighting provide?

     ....

     ....

Top Tips: Gardeners (and farmers) use glass houses because they can create ideal conditions for plant growth, helping them maximise their profits. Make sure you know how gardeners artificially provide plants with light, carbon dioxide and heat.

What Plants Need

Q5 The following passage is taken from an information leaflet produced by a **fertiliser manufacturer** explaining why **minerals** are important to plants. Complete the passage using the words below.

atmosphere	deficiency	low	growth
minerals	high	soil	fertilisers

Each word can be used more than once.

Plants get the .... they need for healthy ....

from the .... are often present at

.... concentrations. If a plant doesn't get enough

.... it can suffer from .... symptoms.

Gardeners can add .... to the soil to make sure that their plants

get all the minerals they need. Different fertilisers contain different amounts of

.... so that gardeners can choose the one that's best for

their plants.

Q6 Vicky is a **garden consultant** — she visits people's gardens to advise them on how to **improve** the **growth** of their plants and lawns.

Mobile Fertiliser Factory

Many of the problems Vicky sees can be solved using **fertilisers** rich in particular minerals. For each of the problems in the table below, say which type of mineral the fertiliser should contain a high concentration of. The first one has been done for you.

Problem	Vicky thinks this is caused by	Fertiliser with a high concentration of
Pauline's plum trees were producing only very small plums.	A problem with the plant's enzymes.	potassium
The leaves on John's pansies turned purple as they got older.	Poor root growth — the plants were not able to respire properly.	
The leaves on Arthur's sweet peas started to discolour.	A problem with the plant's enzymes.	
Brenda planted some lilies, but the leaves came out yellow.	Plants were lacking the green pigment chlorophyll.	
All the plants in Edith's garden have stunted growth. As they got older their leaves turned yellow.	The plant cannot produce enough of the right proteins.	

Intensive Farming

Q1 Simon recently inherited the family farm. An agricultural consultant has advised him to introduce intensive farming methods on the farm in order to increase his crop yield.

a) Complete the paragraph below to explain exactly what is meant by the term 'intensive farming'.

high	maximum	yields	minimum	low

Intensive farming methods are used by farmers to produce bigger and better

.... The aim is to get the .... amount

of food from the .... possible amount of land. One

advantage of intensive farming is that a wide variety of ....

quality foods can be produced at .... prices.

b) Simon plans to use **artificial fertilisers** on his land to increase the crop yield.
Explain how artificial fertilisers help increase crop yield.

....

....

....

Simon's farming methods were intense

c) Simon intends to use **artificial pesticides**, **fungicides** and **herbicides** on the farm.
Complete the table below to explain what each one does and how it will increase the amount of crops Simon produces.

Chemical	What it does	How it improves yield
		Prevents mould damage to crops
	Kills weeds	
Pesticide		

Q2 Jack is a poultry farmer. He intensively farms chickens.
Explain how intensive farming can increase meat production.

....

....

....

Organic Farming

Q1   Farms that are organic can be certified by the **Soil Association**.
Organic farmers use traditional methods of farming than intensive farmers.

a)   State **two** conditions that must be met for a pig farm to be classified as "organic".

1. ....

2. ....

b)   In order to keep soil fertile, organic farmers use **organic fertilisers** instead of artificial fertilisers:

i)   What are organic fertilisers?

....

ii)   Give one benefit of using organic fertilisers instead of artificial fertilisers.

....

iii)   Give one disadvantage of using organic fertilisers instead of artificial fertilisers.

....

Q2   Hugh has been farming **organically** for the past eight years.
Everything grown on his farm carries the Soil Association logo.

a)   Circle the correct word from each pair in the paragraph below
to explain how Hugh controls pests on his farm.

For high crop yields, it is important to kill **pests / weeds** that eat crops. If a
farm is classed as organic, artificial **herbicides / pesticides** cannot be used to
kill pests. Instead, **natural / artificial** pesticides are used, which don't affect
the **pests / environment** as much, as long as they are used responsibly.

uh-oh

b)   Hugh's farm is classed as organic so he cannot use artificial chemicals to control weeds.

i)   What method would an organic farmer use to **control weeds**?

....

ii)   Give one **disadvantage** of the method of organic weed control you stated above.

....

....

Comparing Farming Methods

Q1   Tegan has been farming her land **intensively** for many years. She has
removed hedgerows to make larger fields, which she farms **monoculturally**.

a)   What are the main advantages of intensive farming?

....

b)   Give **two** problems that may arise from removing hedgerows.

1. ....

2. ....

c)   i)   What is meant by the term '**monoculture**'?

....

ii)   Give **two** problems that may be caused by monoculture.

1. ....

2. ....

Q2   Some farmers are changing from **intensive farming** methods to more **traditional methods**.

a)   Match the pairs of statements below to show the **advantages** of organic farming.

Artificial pesticides aren't used

— animals are treated more ethically.

No battery farming

— there is less risk of chemicals remaining on food.

Chemical herbicides and fungicides aren't used

— there is less disruption to food chains.

b)   Complete the paragraph below about organic farming by circling the correct word in each pair.

> Organic farming requires **less / more** space than intensive farming. It is **more / less**
> labour-intensive, which **increases / decreases** production costs. Overall, organic
> farming produces **less / more** food than intensive farming for the same area of land.

Top Tips: In the exam they might ask you to compare different farming methods —
that means you need to know the pros and cons of organic and intensive farming inside out.

Comparing Farming Methods

Q3   Nigel works for the **Environment Agency**. He's investigating reports that a **stream** (which runs alongside a farmer's land) has become covered in a thick blanket of **algae**.

a) **i)** What substance used in agriculture could be the cause of this algal growth?

....

ii) When Nigel analyses the water he finds that the concentrations of one mineral are significantly higher than the others. Which mineral is this most likely to be? Circle the correct answer.

Magnesium	Nitrate	Potassium

b) Put the following sentences in order to describe the problems that this algal growth will cause. The first one has been done for you.

- [ ] Fish die.
- [1] Blanket of algae blocks out sunlight.
- [ ] Decomposers feed on dead plants.
- [ ] Plants die.
- [ ] All the oxygen in the water is used up.

Q4   Amanda works for an environmental consultancy firm. She recently collected samples of **dead organisms** from a pond. She analyses them for the presence of **pesticides**. The diagram below shows the **concentrations** of pesticide Amanda found in each organism.

Concentration of pesticide in microscopic algae: 0.05 ppm → Concentration of pesticide in microscopic animals: 4 ppm → Concentration of pesticide in small fish: 500 ppm → Concentration of pesticide in eels: 2500 ppm

a) Suggest where the pesticide that contaminated the pond might have come from.

....

b) How many times more concentrated was the pesticide in eels than in the microscopic algae?

....

c) Only a low concentration of pesticide was present in the water.
Explain why the concentration of pesticide in eels is so high.

....

....

Comparing Farming Methods

Q5 Read the following passage about organic farming.

> Why does organic food cost so much? Well, it costs more for the farmer to grow crops, partly because it's more labour-intensive. Organic farmers don't use herbicides — so they have to pay people to weed their crops by hand. The use of pesticides is also restricted in organic farming — so the organic farmer risks losing his crops when they get munched up by pests like slugs.
>
> The yield from organic agriculture is lower than from conventional farming. In other words, you get fewer carrots per acre of field. Organic methods rely on growing healthy plants and animals at an unforced pace. For instance, intensively farmed pigs are fed antibiotics, which prevent the spread of disease but which also make them grow faster. Organically farmed pigs are just fed pig food — so they take longer to grow big and become ready for slaughter. Also, organically produced animals are given space to roam around. Intensively farmed animals are often confined in small cages — this uses much less land, so it's cheaper.
>
> So why pay all that extra money — is intensive farming so dreadful? Well, if you like to hear birds singing and see wild flowers and butterflies, blasting the countryside with weedkiller and pesticides is probably not wise. And 'factory farming' isn't much fun if you're a pig or a chicken. It's cheap of course, but it could bring trouble in the long run.

a) What two products are organic farmers not allowed to use?

....

b) Give **three** reasons why organic food is more expensive than its non-organic equivalent.

1. ....

2. ....

3. ....

c) Describe **one** difference between the life of an organically reared pig and an intensively farmed pig.

....

d) Many governments are currently trying to encourage farmers to adopt organic farming practices.

i) Give **one** reason why a government might be trying to increase the number of organic farms.

....

ii) State **two** reasons why many farmers don't change from intensive to organic farming.

1. ....

2. ....

Products from Living Things

Q1   In China many remote villages burn **biogas**. What is biogas and how is it produced?

....

....

Q2   Complete the table to show which **living thing** each of
the following is made from and give a **possible use**.

	comes from	used for
leather		
glucose		
rubber		
aspirin		
wood		
cotton		

Q3   Brian is a **research scientist** who is investigating possible new **antibiotics**.

a)   How are antibiotics made?

....

b)   Name one antibiotic.

....

Q4   Microbes can be **modified** to produce substances like **human insulin** to treat **diabetes**.
Give the name of the process by which microbes can be modified to produce insulin.

....

Top Tips: We get loads of stuff from living things — from bread and cheese to fuels
and medicines. Microorganisms play a really important role in producing some of these things.
Make sure you learn all the facts — in the exam they'll expect you to be able to name the type
of organism that produces certain products.

Products from Living Things

Q5   A **cheese manufacturer** is making a batch of Froggart's mature cheddar.
Rearrange the following sentences to explain the cheese making process.

☐ The solid curds are separated from the liquid whey.

1 A culture of bacteria is added to warm milk.

☐ The bacteria cause the formation of curds in the milk.

☐ More bacteria are added and the curds are left to ripen.

Q6   Daisy has a **strawberry yoghurt** in her packed lunch. A label on the side of the
yoghurt pot says that the milk used to make the yoghurt has been **pasteurised**.

  a) **i)** Why is the milk pasteurised?

  ....

  ii) Describe the pasteurisation process.

  ....

  b) Complete the paragraph below using the words provided to describe how Daisy's
yoghurt has been manufactured. Each word can be used more than once.

lactose	fermenter	clot	lactic	bacteria

  A culture of .... is added to some milk and the mixture is

  heated in a .... The .... convert the

  .... sugar in the milk into .... acid,

  which causes the milk to .... and solidify into yoghurt.

Q7   **Barton Bakery** is baking their famous bacon-flavoured loaves of **bread**.
One of the most important ingredients when making bread is **yeast**.

  a) What would happen to Barton Bakery's bread if they did not add any yeast?

  ....

  b) What **gas** is produced by the yeast that causes small holes to form in the bread?

  ....

  c) Name another substance that is produced by the yeast.

  Think about what drinks yeast is used to make.

  ....

Products from Living Things

Q8   Sharon likes to make her own **wine**. The picture below shows the equipment that she uses.

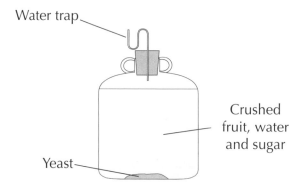

Water trap

Crushed fruit, water and sugar

Yeast

a)   Complete the word equation for fermentation.

sugar $\longrightarrow$ .... + ...

b)   Whilst the wine is fermenting Sharon needs to keep it warm. Why is this?

....

c)   When fermentation is complete, Sharon will bottle the wine.
Before the wine is bottled she filters it. Suggest why she does this.

....

Q9   Reg is the head brewer at a **brewery**.
He supervises the manufacture of **beer** from **grain**.

a)   Where does the sugar for fermentation come from?

....

b)   What two things must the brewery workers do to the grain before it can be added to the fermentation vessels?

1. ....

2. ....

c)   Why are hops added to the fermentation mixture? Underline the correct answer.

To start the process of fermentation.   To break down the starch in the grain.

To make the beer fizzy.   To give the beer its flavour.

Selecting Characteristics

Q1 Jeremy is a beef farmer. To maximise his profits he **selectively breeds** cows that have the highest meat yields.

a) Number the sentences below to show the stages of selective breeding in the correct order.

- [ ] Breed them with each other.
- [ ] Select the best offspring.
- [ ] Continue the process over many generations.
- [ ] Combine with the best you already have and breed again.
- [1] Select individuals with the best characteristics.

Ruminant Romance

Find the bull of your dreams   I can be quite a picky cow   Y the week: Daisy

b) Complete the following sentences by circling the correct word(s) in each pair.

i) Selective breeding increases / decreases the number of different alleles in a population.

ii) Animals in a herd that have been bred selectively will be closely / distantly related.

iii) If a new disease appears few / all of the animals are likely to be affected.

iv) Selective breeding leads to an increase / a decrease in the gene pool.

Q2 **Agricultural scientists** can use **genetic engineering** to modify plants and animals to have **desired characteristics**. Complete the passage to describe the process of genetic engineering. Each word can be used once, more than once or not at all.

characteristics	early	genes	fats	late

Genetic engineering usually involves moving .... from one organism to another. This transfer is done in the .... stages of development. The .... that the plant or animal develops depend on the .... inserted.

Q3 Heather is a member of a group that campaigns **against** genetically engineered foods. Suggest **three** reasons why Heather might think that genetic engineering is wrong.

1. ....

2. ....

3. ....

Top Tips: The possible uses of genetic engineering really are endless — long life tomatoes, animals that produce drugs... The big problem is that the long term consequences are still unknown.

Selecting Characteristics

Q4   Kim works for a large **agricultural research** firm. One of the tasks
she carries out on a daily basis is **tissue culture**. The diagram below
shows the process of producing **cloned maize plants** by tissue culture.

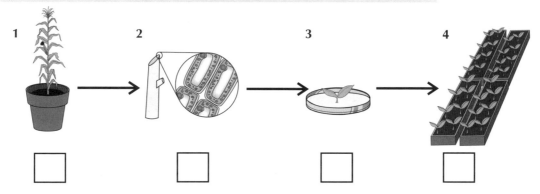

a)   Match the following statements to the stages in the diagram by writing the letter in the correct box.

A Cells removed from growing tip.

B Clones grown in potting compost.

C Parent plant with desired characteristics.

D Cells placed on sterile growing substance containing hormones.

b)   The company Kim works for produces maize on a commercial scale. Each plant costs an average
of £0.03 to produce. Another company uses traditional methods — each plant costs an average of
£0.07 to produce. Each company produces 50,000 plants per year. How much does the company
Kim works for save per year by using tissue culture methods rather than traditional methods?

....

Q5   Clive farms two small **beef herds**. Herd A is made up entirely of cloned offspring (using
embryo transplantation). Traditional **selective breeding** techniques are used on herd B.

a)   What is the advantage of producing embryos by embryo transplantation compared to
selective breeding?

....

b)   Tick the boxes to say whether the following apply to herd A or herd B.   **Herd A   Herd B   Neither**

i)   The offspring are clones of each other.   ☐   ☐   ☐

ii) The offspring are clones of their parents.   ☐   ☐   ☐

iii) The offspring are genetically different from their parents and each other. ☐   ☐   ☐

c)   Clive is contacted by DEFRA who inform him that a new strain of Bovine Tuberculosis has been
discovered. Which herd should Simon take greater measures to protect? Explain your answer.

*Bovine TB is
an infectious
disease.*

....

....

Selecting Characteristics

Q6   Read the following passage about **genetic modification**.

Genetic engineering has been a controversial issue since GM crops were first introduced for commercial production in 1996. Despite this, by 2001 GM crops covered more than 109.2 million acres worldwide. U.S. farmers are by far the largest producers of GM or 'biotech' crops, producing over 60% of GM crops worldwide. The main crops include corn, soybeans and cotton. The table opposite shows the percentage of planted crops in the U.S. that are genetically modified.

Crop	% of planted crops that were GM in U.S. in 2001
corn	26
soybean	68
cotton	69

The debate about these genetically modified crops continues to rage despite the fact that they are already grown in huge numbers. The benefits seem clear to the U.S. farming community, which is thought to save millions of pounds each year by using pest-resistant crops rather than chemical pesticides.

Scientists are still unsure about the effect of GM crops on wildlife. A study by Iowa State University in the U.S. has reported that pollen from GM corn is toxic to Monarch caterpillars in the laboratory. The caterpillars were seven times more likely to die when they ate plants dusted with pollen from GM corn rather than normal corn.

The effect on wildlife is only one of the many arguments against the growing of GM crops. There is an increasing worry that the genetic material from GM crops will be transferred into wild plants, creating so-called 'superweeds'. Also, many believe that only the multinational biotech companies will reap the rewards from producing GM crops. However, some GM crops such as rice that increases levels of Vitamin A have been designed for countries where malnutrition is rife.

As the advantages and disadvantages of growing genetically modified crops become increasingly clear, the problem is deciding whether this is still a risk we are willing to take.

a)   What is the main benefit to farmers using GM crops?

   ....

b)   Despite public concern, the multinational biotech companies are continuing to develop GM crops. Suggest a reason why.

   ....

c)   Suggest **two** reasons why a farmer might not want to change to using GM crops.

   1.   ....

   2.   ....

d)   State **one** way that the development of GM crops has benefited society.

   ....

e)   State **two** reasons why the accidental creation of 'superweeds' is a cause for concern.

   1.   ....

   2.   ....

Useful Chemicals from the Ground

Q1   The picture below shows Julie making a cup of coffee. Six items are labelled
— two of these are **elements**, two are **compounds** and two are **mixtures**.

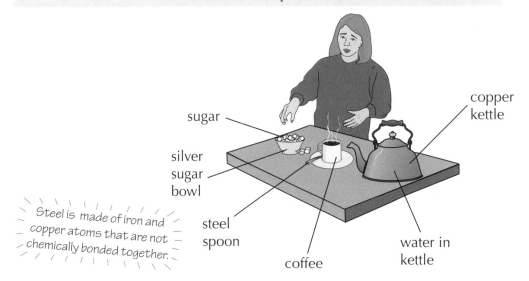

sugar

copper
kettle

silver
sugar
bowl

Steel is made of iron and copper atoms that are not chemically bonded together.

steel
spoon

water in
kettle

coffee

a)   The two elements are .... and ....

b)   The two compounds are .... and ....

c)   The two mixtures are .... and ....

Q2   Katie has drawn diagrams to represent **elements**, **compounds** and **mixtures**.
Match the letter of each diagram to the types of substances given.

A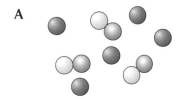

B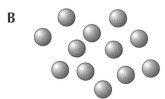

C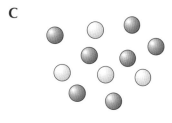

D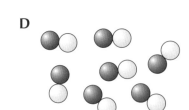

a)   Element ....

b)   Compound ....

c)   Mixture of elements ....

d)   Mixture of elements and compounds ....

<u>Top Tips:</u>   You need to be able to show the examiner that you know what elements,
compounds and mixtures are. They've got some pretty important differences.

Useful Chemicals from the Ground

Q3 Tick the boxes to show whether the statements are **true** or **false**.

	True	False
a) Elements, mixtures and compounds are made up of atoms.	☐	☐
b) Elements contain only one type of atom.	☐	☐
c) Mixtures contain different types of atoms bonded together chemically.	☐	☐
d) Mixtures are easier to separate than compounds.	☐	☐
e) Limestone is a mixture.	☐	☐

Q4 Use the words below to fill in the gaps in the passage.

compounds   elements   sulfur   calcium   gold   building   unreactive

Sulfur and gold are useful .... that are mined or quarried out of the ground. They are both ...., so are usually found in an uncombined state. .... can be found near volcanoes, and .... is sometimes found in river beds.

Limestone and marble are useful .... that are mined or quarried out of the ground. They are both forms of .... carbonate, and are used extensively in .... construction.

Q5 List two uses for **sulfur**, **gold**, **limestone** and **marble**.

a) Sulfur

1. ....

2. ....

b) Gold

1. ....

2. ....

c) Limestone

1. ....

2. ....

d) Marble

1. ....

2. ....

Rock Salt and Crude Oil

Q1   Mr Nelson is a science teacher. He would like to do a laboratory experiment with his pupils to demonstrate how **salt** is separated from **rock salt**. He has found this simple method for an experiment in an old science textbook:

1. Dissolve the rock salt in water.

2. Filter the solution.

3. Evaporate the filtrate.

Look at the diagrams below.

A 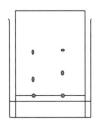   B 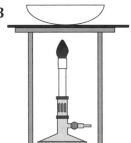   C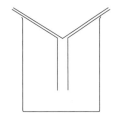

a)   **i)**   Which diagram shows the apparatus needed for step **2** of the experiment? ....

     ii)   What is removed during this step of the experiment? ....

b)   **i)**   Which diagram shows the apparatus needed for step **3** of the experiment? ....

     ii)   What is removed during this step of the experiment? ....

Q2   Gillian is a **petrochemical scientist** who works for an **oil company**. She has been asked to give a presentation to school children to explain **how** and **why oil is refined**.

a)   The notes Gillian prepared for her presentation have been dropped and jumbled up. Write numbers in the boxes to show the correct order of the sentences.

     A The different fractions in the crude oil condense at different temperatures.   ☐

     B Crude oil is formed from the buried remains of animals and plants. It is extracted from the ground by drilling.   ☐

     C The different chemicals are collected from different parts of the column — the bottom of the column is the hottest, and the top of the column is coolest. The different chemicals are used for different things.   ☐

     D The crude oil is heated until it evaporates, and the vapours rise up the column.   ☐

b)   What is the name of the **process** that separates crude oil into different chemicals?

....

Metals

Q1   What is a **metal ore**?

....

....

Q2   Joseph completes an experiment in his science class to see which metals
he can extract from their ores using **charcoal** (a source of carbon).
He tests **copper oxide**, **lead oxide**, **iron oxide** and **aluminium oxide**.

Joseph places one spatula of the metal oxide
in an ignition tube, and carefully adds one
spatula of charcoal powder. He then heats
the ignition tube for five minutes using a
Bunsen burner. After the tube has cooled,
he examines it carefully.

ignition tube

charcoal

metal
oxide

Bunsen burner

a)   If Joseph successfully extracts a metal from its oxide, what should he expect to see in the ignition
tube after the experiment?

....

b)   Joseph extracts copper, lead, and iron from their oxides, but **not aluminium**.
Why can't aluminium be extracted using charcoal?

....

....

c)   Write a word equation for the extraction of **lead** from lead oxide using charcoal.

....

d)   In the reaction in part c),

    i)   what is reduced? ....

    ii) what is the reducing agent? ....

    iii) Suggest another reducing agent that could be used. ....

Top Tips: Metals are usually found in the ground in compounds like lead oxide or
iron oxide. A lot of metals can be separated from their compounds using a reducing agent.

Metals

Q4 Melanie is an environmental scientist who works for a **copper mine** in Africa. Copper ore is removed from the mine, and **copper carbonate** is extracted from this ore. The copper carbonate is transported to the UK, where it is further reduced to produce **copper**. The copper is sold in the UK at a price of £1000 per tonne.

a) Melanie has been asked to suggest ways the mine can increase its profits. She begins by working out the cost of producing **1 tonne** of **copper**.

Cost of mining 200 tonnes of copper ore.	£200
Cost of extracting 2 tonnes of copper carbonate from 200 tonnes of copper ore.	£200
Cost of transporting 2 tonnes of copper carbonate to the UK.	£60
Cost of reducing 2 tonnes of copper carbonate to produce 1 tonne of copper.	£200

i) What is the **total cost** of producing 1 tonne of copper?

....

ii) Using the information in the table, what is the **percentage** of copper carbonate in copper ore?

....

iii) Melanie suggests that the copper carbonate is further reduced in Africa instead of in the UK. How will this help the mine increase profits?

....

....

b) The mine invests in developing facilities to reduce the copper carbonate locally.

i) How will this benefit the **local people**?

....

ii) Why might this be bad for the **environment**?

....

iii) The cost of processing 2 tonnes of copper carbonate to produce 1 tonne of copper locally is £100. The cost of transporting 1 tonne of copper to the UK is £30. Calculate how much **profit** the mine will now make selling 1 tonne of pure copper.

.... 〜 Work out how much it costs 〜
                                                                                        ～ to produce in total first. ～

....

Top Tips: Metals are much more useful after they've been extracted from their ores. Make sure that you understand how a metal oxide can be reduced and can write equations for the extraction of metals. It's also an idea to learn why extracting metals can be bad for the environment.

Fossil Fuels

Q1   Fill in the blanks in the paragraph below.

Coal, oil and .... are all .... fuels.

They are formed from the remains of animals and plants over ....

of years. Energy is released from the fuels by .... them

— this energy originally came from the ....

Q2   The pie chart shows **energy supplies** in the UK.

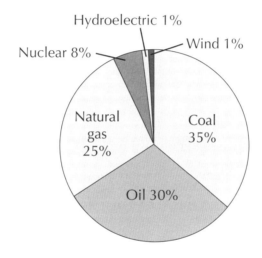

a)   What percentage of the energy is supplied by fossil fuels?

....

b)   Why will the amount of energy supplied by fossil fuels have to be reduced in the future?

....

Q3   The diagram below shows what happens when **natural gas** (methane) burns in air.

a)   What is A? ....   **b)**   What is B? ....

Fossil Fuels

Q4 James is an environmental scientist working for a coal-fired power station. He has been investigating **alternative fuels** to use.

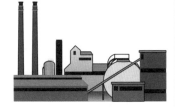

Fuel	Cost (pence per kg)	Heat Content (kJ per kg)
Coal	11	34 000
Wood	5	21 000
Ethanol	130	30 000
Methane (natural gas)	60	56 000

a) Which of the fuels in the table will release the most energy when burnt? ....

b) Which **two** fuels in the table are non-renewable fossil fuels?

....

c) Give one non-environmental problem associated with the use of non-renewable fuels.

....

d) All four fuels in the table contain **carbon**.

   i) What gas will this form when the fuel is burnt? ....

   ii) What environmental problem does this gas cause? ....

e) Suggest **two** reasons why James wants to switch from coal to a different fuel.

   1. ....

   2. ....

f) Ethanol is obtained from plants, and is the cleanest burning fuel in the table. Suggest **two** reasons why James is not keen on switching to ethanol.

   1. ....

   2. ....

g) James is also investigating ways of reducing the **sulfur dioxide emissions** from the power station. He could invest in **flue gas desulfurisation** equipment that would reduce emissions by 90%.

   i) Why does James want to reduce sulfur dioxide emissions?

   ....

   ....

   ii) The flue gas desulfurisation equipment will reduce the efficiency of the power station by 2%. What does this mean in terms of the amount of coal burnt at the power station?

   ....

Alternatives to Fossil Fuels

Q1   Look at the list of **energy resources** below.

nuclear   wave   coal   hydroelectric   solar   gas   tidal   oil   wind

a)   Circle the resources on the list that are renewable.

b)   Which two energy resources in the list involve seawater?

....

Q2   **Waves** can be used to drive a generator, which produces electricity.

a)   What are the advantages of wave power? Circle the two correct answers.

no pollution   very reliable   low set up costs   no fuel costs

b)   What are the disadvantages of wave power? Circle the two correct answers.

high pollution   high set-up costs   unreliable   high running costs

Q3   It has been proposed that a large **tidal barrage** be built on an estuary in Scotland. A scientist has written a report about the potential effects of this on the surrounding **environment**.

a)   The following statements explain how a tidal barrage works but they are in the wrong order. Put them in the correct order by writing numbers in the boxes.

The water is released from the barrage at a controlled rate. ☐

The tide comes in. ☐

The turbines drive a generator that produces electricity. ☐

The tide is held back by the barrage. ☐

The water drives turbines as it is released. ☐

b)   Building the barrage would flood a large area surrounding the estuary.
How might this affect the **wildlife** in the area?

....

c)   How might construction of the barrage affect **boating access** in the area?

....

d)   A tidal barrage would cost £7 000 000 and could provide 8 000 000 kW hours of electricity per year. 1 kW hour of electricity would cost £0.02 to produce and could be sold for £0.07. How many years would it take to cover the cost of building the barrage?

....

....

Alternatives to Fossil Fuels

Q4   A coal-fired power station on the north coast of Scotland is going to be replaced by **wind turbines**. The power station used to produce 4 000 000 kW of electricity a year. Jenny is an environmental scientist who is involved in choosing the location of the wind turbines. Three sites have been proposed, two of which are offshore. **Site A** has an average wind speed of **8 m/s**, **Site B** has an average wind speed of **9 m/s**, and **Site C** has an average wind speed of **11 m/s**.

   a)   Which proposed site would produce the most electricity? ....

   b)   What are the benefits of placing the wind turbines offshore?
   Tick **two** boxes from the list below.

   It is less likely people will complain about the noise. ☐

   It will cost less. ☐

   It doesn't matter if you pollute the sea. ☐

   There is generally more wind. ☐

Q5   Answer the following questions by putting a circle around the correct answer.

   a)   Which power source can have a large impact on the environment through flooding?

   wind   **solar**   **hydroelectric**   **nuclear**

   b)   Which power source can respond immediately to increases in power demand?

   wind   **solar**   **hydroelectric**   **nuclear**

   c)   Which power source does not pollute the environment once built?

   wind   **solar**   **hydroelectric**   **all three**

Q6   Karen uses 3000 kW hours of electricity a year, which costs her £250. She is considering buying **solar panels** for the roof of her house. A 3 m² solar panel would cost her £2000, and could produce 1500 kW hours of electricity a year.

   a)   How much money could the solar panel save Karen every year?

   ....

   b)   Explain how fitting the solar panel would be good for the environment.

   ....

   ....

Alternatives to Fossil Fuels

Q7   Circle the correct word from each pair in the paragraph
below to explain how **nuclear power** works.

> Nuclear power is a renewable / non-renewable energy resource. It involves
>
> splitting atoms by a process called nuclear fission / fusion. This releases
>
> small / large amounts of heat energy from small / large amounts of neon / uranium.
>
> The energy produced is used to heat oil / water, to turn it into steam. The steam
>
> drives a turbine, which in turn drives a generator, which produces fuel / electricity.

Q8   The table below shows the amount of **carbon dioxide** produced by different fuels.

Fuel	Amount of carbon dioxide (tonnes) produced by 1 tonne of fuel
Coal	2.0
Oil	2.5
Gas	2.5
Uranium	0

a)   Which fuel, in the table above, does not produce any carbon dioxide?

....

b)   5000 tonnes of oil need to be burnt to produce the same amount of energy as 1 tonne of uranium.
How much carbon dioxide would be released by burning this amount of oil?

....

c)   Name two environmental problems that nuclear power can cause.

1. ....

2. ....

Top Tips: Renewable energy resources are pretty crucial when it comes to trying to stop
climate change, but they're not without their downsides. It's not enough to learn about why it's
important to have alternatives to fossil fuels — make sure you know some of their problems too.

Comparing Energy Resources

Q1 Answer the following questions about energy resources.

a) Which energy resource listed below pollutes the atmosphere? Circle the correct answer.

nuclear   hydroelectric   gas   wind

b) List **three** factors that should be considered when choosing an energy resource.

1. ....

2. ....

3. ....

Q2 The map below shows a small island. Five sites are labelled A - E. These are the proposed sites of different **energy developments**. Environmental scientists are assessing the potential of each site.

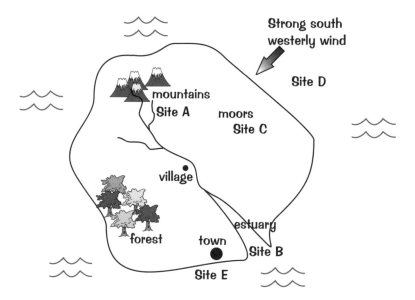

a) Which site would be most suitable for a **tidal barrage**? Explain why.

....

b) Which site would be most suitable for a **hydroelectric power station**? Explain why.

....

c) Which two sites would be most suitable for a **wind farm**? Explain why.

....

....

d) Sites D and E are both being considered as the location for a **wave powered station**. Which of these two sites would you recommend? Explain your answer.

....

Generating Electricity

Q1   The diagram below shows a **power station**.

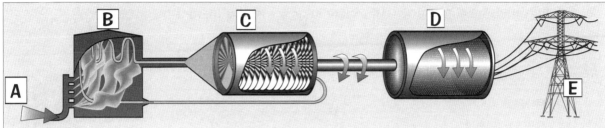

a)   Draw lines to match up the parts of the diagram with the appropriate sentences.

A

B

C

D

E

Steam is used to turn a turbine.

The electricity is delivered via a network of cables.

The fuel is burnt and the heat energy is used to boil water.

Fuel (e.g. coal, oil, or gas) enters the boiler.

The turbine rotates a generator to create electricity.

b)   Energy is converted into different forms (including kinetic, electrical, heat and chemical energy) within a power station.

    i)   Which type of energy is contained in the **fuel**? ....

    ii)   Which type of energy is produced in part **B**? ....

    iii) Which type of energy is produced in part **C**? ....

    iv)   Which type of energy does the power station produce? ....

c)   When energy is converted into another type in a power station, some of the energy is lost. For every 100 joules (J) of energy stored in the fuel, 10 J are lost in the boiler, 30 J are lost in cooling water, and 5 J are lost by the generator.

    i)   What is the **useful** energy output from 100 J of fuel?

Work out how much energy is left over.

        ....

    ii)   What is the **efficiency** of the power station in %?

Using your answer to i), work out what percentage of the energy in the fuel is useful.

        ....

d)   What is the National Grid?

....

....

....

The Origins of Life on Earth

Q1 The first gases that formed the atmosphere came from **volcanoes**. The table below shows the composition of volcanic gases, and the composition of gases in the atmosphere today. Use the table to answer the questions below.

Gas	% in volcanic gases	% in atmosphere
nitrogen	5	78
oxygen	0	21
carbon dioxide	11	0.04
water vapour	20	0 – 0.07

a) Which gas released by volcanoes has built up in the atmosphere over time?

....

b) Which gas present in the atmosphere today could **not** have come from volcanoes?

....

c) Which gas released by volcanoes created the oceans? ....

Q2 The graph shows the percentage of two different gases in the **atmosphere** over the last four billion years.

a) **i)** What is Gas A?

....

ii) What evolved two billion years ago and started to produce Gas A?

....

b) **i)** What is Gas B?

....

ii) What process, involving plants, has decreased the percentage of this gas in the atmosphere?

....

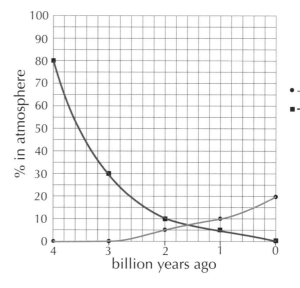

Q3 The order of the **planets**, starting with those closest to the Sun, is given in the list below. **Earth** is missing from the list. Draw an arrow on the list to show the position of Earth.

Mercury   Venus   Mars   Jupiter   Saturn   Uranus   Neptune

Human Impact on the Earth

Q1 Scientists at the Mauna Loa observatory in Hawaii have measured **atmospheric carbon dioxide (CO_2)** levels for over **60 years**. The graph below shows how the level of CO_2 in the atmosphere has changed since 1960.

a) What was the level of CO_2 in the atmosphere in **1980**?

....

b) By how much has the level of CO_2 in the atmosphere risen between 1960 and 2000?

....

c) If the level of CO_2 in the atmosphere continues to increase at the rate shown, how much CO_2 will be in the atmosphere in **2010**?

....

Q2 There is good evidence that the Earth is gradually **heating up**, at least partly because of increasing levels of **greenhouse gases** (such as carbon dioxide) in the atmosphere.

a) i) Give one way **human** activity is increasing the level of CO_2 in the atmosphere.

....

ii) Give one **natural** activity that releases CO_2 into the atmosphere.

....

b) Explain how increased levels of greenhouse gases in the atmosphere cause the Earth to heat up.

....

....

c) List two problems that may result from the Earth's temperature increasing.

1. ....

2. ....

d) Why is it hard for scientists to predict exactly what will happen to the climate in the future?

....

Human Impact on the Earth

Q3   Gillian is an **environmental scientist** who has been monitoring the **pH** of rainwater near a **power station** over a twelve month period. Here are some of her results:

Month	pH of rainwater
January	4.3
March	5.1
May	5.4
July	5.7
September	5.3
November	4.5

The lower the pH number, the more acidic the water.

a)   In which month was the rain most acidic?

....

b)   Name **two** gases released by power stations that can cause acid rain.

1. ....

2. ....

c)   List **two** problems that can be caused by acid rain.

1. ....

2. ....

d)   The samples of rainwater are only slightly acidic. What safety precautions should Gillian take when handling stronger samples of acid?

....

e)   What could Gillian measure to monitor the effects of acid rain in the local area?

....

Q4   **Burning fossil fuels** contributes to problems such as **global warming** and **acid rain**.
In the last few hundred years the amount of fossil fuels being burnt has increased rapidly.

Give **two** reasons why the amount of fossil fuels being burnt has increased so rapidly in the last few hundred years.

1. ....

2. ....

Human Impact on the Earth

Q5 The **environment health** services have received a number of reports that a **copper mine** is polluting a **local river**. They send a scientist out to investigate.

a) List **three** ways mining can damage the environment.

1. ....

2. ....

3. ....

b) For every 1000 kg of copper ore taken out of the ground, only 5 kg of pure copper is obtained.

i) How many kg of waste is produced from 1000 kg of copper ore?

....

ii) What percentage of copper ore becomes waste?

....

c) The environmental scientist tested samples of water from the river for levels of certain **toxic chemicals**. The results from these tests are shown in the table below.

chemical	level of chemical in river (mg/l)	
	1 km from copper mine	10 km from copper mine
copper	2.3	1.1
zinc	1.3	0.7
arsenic	0.4	0.1
cadmium	0.1	0.05
lead	0.9	0.5
mercury	0.08	0.05

i) How do the toxic chemicals get into the river?

....

ii) Which chemical is present in the **highest** concentration 1 km from the copper mine?

....

iii) What happens to the level of pollution as you get further away from the mine?

....

iv) How might these chemicals affect the animals and plants that live in the river?

....

....

Human Impact on the Earth

Q6 Because of the effects it can have on the **environment** it is important to **monitor** the amount of **waste produced**. The pie chart below shows the different types of waste produced in the UK.

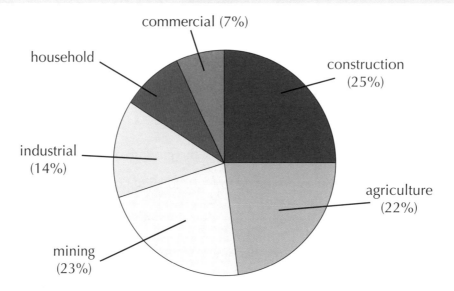

commercial (7%)

household

construction (25%)

industrial (14%)

agriculture (22%)

mining (23%)

a) Which **three** industries in the UK produce the most waste?

....

b) What percentage of UK waste is household waste?

....

c) Most waste ends up in landfill sites. Give one **environmental problem** with landfill sites.

....

d) One way of dealing with waste is to **recycle** it. In 2004, 17% of waste was recycled.

   i) Name two types of material that can be recycled.

      1. ....

      2. ....

   ii) Give two **benefits** of recycling waste.

      1. ....

      2. ....

e) If 100 million tonnes of waste was produced in 2004, what mass was recycled?

....

Top Tips: We produce far too much waste. Just think how much packaging there is when you get something like a TV or even a microwave curry — the more that can be recycled, the better.

Mixed Questions for Sections 2.4 and 2.5

Q1 Vincent is a **vulcanologist**. He studies current and historic **eruptions** of volcanoes around the world.

a) i) What causes volcanoes to erupt?

....

ii) Why is it important for scientists to constantly **monitor** volcanic activity?

....

b) **Sulfur** is often found in the ground near volcanoes. It's not very reactive so can often be used straight from the ground. Which of the following substances can also be used straight from the ground without further processing? Circle the correct answer(s).

bauxite   marble   gold   crude oil

c) Volcanoes played an important role in the **evolution** of the **atmosphere** and life on Earth. Put numbers in the boxes next to the following sentences so they're in the correct order to describe the evolution of the atmosphere. The first one has been done for you.

> ☐ Plants evolved.
>
> 1 The Earth's surface was molten — any atmosphere boiled away.
>
> ☐ The ozone layer formed.
>
> ☐ Oxygen levels increased and carbon dioxide levels decreased.
>
> ☐ The surface cooled to form a thin crust but volcanoes continued to erupt, releasing mostly CO_2.

d) Plants have a number of cells that are specially adapted for **photosynthesis**. Describe how palisade leaf cells are adapted for photosynthesis.

....

....

....

e) One of the products of photosynthesis is **glucose**, a sugar with the formula $C_6H_{12}O_6$.

i) How many different elements does glucose contain?

....

ii) Is glucose an element, a mixture or a compound?

....

Countryside & Environmental Management

Mixed Questions for Sections 2.4 and 2.5

Q2   Lance farms his land **intensively** but he's thinking of changing to **organic** farming. Lance must take a lot of factors into account when making this decision.

a)   State why plants need each of the following minerals.

i) Nitrates ....

ii) Magnesium ....

b)   Organic farmers must follow different **guidelines** from those followed by intensive farmers. Tick the boxes to show whether the following statements apply to organic or intensive farms.

Organic   Intensive

i)   Artificial fertilisers are used. ☐   ☐

ii) Mechanical weeding is used. ☐   ☐

iii) Animals are free to roam outside for a set time. ☐   ☐

iv) Artificial pesticides and herbicides are used. ☐   ☐

c)   Food produced by organic farmers is increasing in popularity even though it tends to be more expensive than food produced intensively.

i)   Suggest a reason why organically produced food is increasing in popularity.

....

ii) Why might this change as the world's population continues to increase?

Think about which farming method can produce more food.

....

....

....

Q3   Globally, 39% of electricity is generated in **coal fired power stations**. Many countries are attempting to replace coal fired power stations with '**cleaner**' alternatives because of concern over **climate change**.

Pedal faster Geoff

a)   Give one **advantage** and one **disadvantage** of each of the following.

i)   Nuclear power ....

....

ii) Hydroelectricity ....

....

b)   One possible option is the use of **biogas**. How is biogas produced?

....

Countryside & Environmental Management

Mixed Questions for Sections 2.4 and 2.5

Q4 Janet is an environmental officer at a **mine**. Part of her job is to ensure that no **toxic chemicals** are released into the surrounding environment.

a) **i)** Give **one** disadvantage of mining other than the release of toxic chemicals.

....

ii) Give **one** social benefit of mining.

....

b) One method of removing toxic waste from contaminated land is phytoremediation — where plants are used to absorb the toxic chemicals.

i) Plants absorb the chemicals through their roots.
Describe how plant roots are adapted for absorption.

....

....

ii) Plants which absorb the most chemicals can be selected and then cloned.
Give one advantage and one disadvantage of cloning plants.

....

....

Q5 **Fossil fuels** are hydrocarbons — they are made up of only **hydrogen** and **carbon** atoms. The majority of fossil fuels we use are burnt in power stations to produce **electricity**.

a) Write a general word equation for the complete combustion of a hydrocarbon.

....

b) Generating electricity can be quite an expensive process. Suggest a reason for this.

....

....

c) **i)** How is an increasing world population likely to affect energy production?

....

....

ii) Which of the following could be caused by burning fossil fuels?
Underline the correct answer(s)

acid rain   rising sea levels   increased volcanic activity   changing weather patterns

Chemical Building Blocks

Q1 George is a **scuba diving** instructor. When he goes diving he takes a bottle of **oxygen** so that he can breathe underwater.

Label this diagram of an oxygen atom.

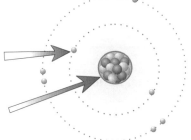

a) ....

b) ....

Q2 Draw lines to match up the statements below to the parts of an atom that they describe.

| These are found in the nucleus along with protons. | | Electrons |

| The atomic number is the number of these in an element. | | Protons |

| These move around the nucleus in shells. | | Neutrons |

Q3 Look at the table below and then answer the questions.

Element	No. protons in nucleus
Sodium	11
Magnesium	12
Chlorine	17
Aluminium	13

a) Which element has the **largest** atomic number?

....

b) What is the atomic number of **sodium**?

....

Q4 Katya is a scientist who tests **fizzy mineral water** to make sure there are no harmful chemicals in it. Draw lines to show whether the substances Katya has found are **atoms**, **molecules** or **ions**.

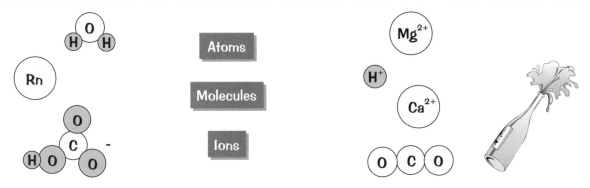

Top Tips: Atoms are all pretty much the same in terms of their basic structure — there's some stuff in the middle and some more stuff whizzing round the outside. Easy.

Chemical Symbols

Q1 Simon is a **meteorologist**. Every day he produces a report on the **air quality** at the weather station where he works.

Write out the chemical formula for each of the molecules below that Simon finds in an air sample.

a) 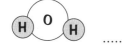 ....

b) ....

c)  ....

d) ....

Q2 **Sunnydale Petrochemicals** manufacture products from **crude oil**.

Circle the correct chemical formula for each of their products below.

a)

4CH   CH$_4$ CH$_2$CH$_2$ C$_4$H

b)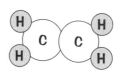

CH$_2$CO$_2$ CH$_4$ C$_2$H$_4$ C$_4$H$_2$

c)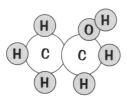

C$_2$H$_4$O   COH$_5$ CH$_2$CH$_2$O   C$_2$H$_5$OH

d)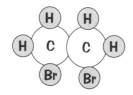

(H$_2$CBr)$_2$ CH$_4$ CH$_2$BrCH$_2$Br   C$_4$H$_4$Br$_2$

Q3 Write the **chemical equation** for each of the reactions below.

Check your answers by counting the number of atoms of each element.

a)  ....

b) 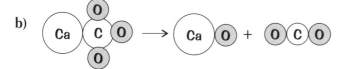 ....

c)  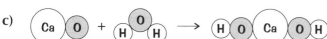 ....

Chemical Equations

Q1 Fill in the blanks using the words below to complete the passage about **balancing equations**.

| chemicals | arranged | big | equation | atom |

In chemical reactions, atoms are not created or destroyed — they're just

.... differently. Chemical formulas tell you how many of

each type of .... are in a molecule. It is important to balance

a chemical .... so that the number of each type of atom is

the same on both sides. When you do this, you can't change formulas like CO_2

to CO_3 for example. Instead you need to change the ....

numbers that you write in front of the ....

Q2 Katy is an **energy consultant** investigating how to make kitchen cookers safer and more efficient. The gas burnt in kitchen cookers, **methane**, has the chemical formula CH_4. When methane burns, it reacts with oxygen in the air to make carbon dioxide and water.

a) Which **two** elements are found in a molecule of methane?

....

b) How many atoms of these elements are found in each molecule of methane?

....

c) Write a **balanced symbol equation** to show the burning of methane.

....

Q3 Only one of the equations on the right is **balanced correctly**. Circle the one correctly balanced one.

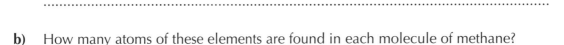

$Na + O_2 \rightarrow Na_2O$

$Na + O_2 \rightarrow Na_2O_2$

$2Na + O_2 \rightarrow Na_2O$

$4Na + O_2 \rightarrow 2Na_2O$

Q4 **Balance** the following equations by inserting numbers in front of the chemicals where necessary.

a) $Zn + HCl \rightarrow ZnCl_2 + H_2$

b) $Fe + Cl_2 \rightarrow FeCl_3$

c) $K + H_2O \rightarrow KOH + H_2$

d) $Al + O_2 \rightarrow Al_2O_3$

Top Tips: Chemical equations have a nasty whiff of maths about them, but as long as you make sure **both sides** of the arrow are **balanced**, there's not really much to go wrong.

Chemical Bonding and Properties

Q1 Fill in the blanks using the words below to complete the passage about the **structure of metals**.

giant	conductivity	metallic	free	electrons

Metals are held together by .... bonds. These strong bonds hold the

metal atoms together in a .... structure. In this structure, some

.... in each atom can move about the metal structure, which

creates a 'sea' of .... electrons. This structure causes the properties

of metals, such as their high melting points and good electrical ....

Q2 In order to use materials effectively, **materials scientists** need to understand their properties.
Below are some **properties of metals** and descriptions of how **atoms** are arranged in metals.

Properties of metals	How atoms are arranged in metals
Malleable	Strong bond between atoms
High density	Free electrons between atoms
High melting point	Atoms packed close together
Good at conducting electricity	Layers of atoms can slide over each other

a) Draw lines to match the properties of metals to the arrangement of atoms which cause it.

b) Name one property of metals which is not listed above.

....

Q3 Stephen is a **materials scientist**. He is designing a computer
program that will work out whether an element is a **metal** or
a **non-metal** according to the **properties** that the user inputs.

Stephen uses the information below about elements to test the program.
Tick the boxes to show which are metals and which are non-metals

Element	State at room temperature	Heat conductivity	Melting point / °C	Density g/cm³	Metal	Non-metal
Argon	Gas	Poor	−189	0.01		
Bromine	Liquid	Very poor	−7	3.1		
Calcium	Solid	Very Good	842	1.5		
Lead	Solid	Poor	327	11.3		
Phosphorus	Solid	Very poor	44	1.8		
Potassium	Solid	Good	63	0.9		

Chemical Bonding and Properties

Q4 Fill in the blanks using the words below to complete the passage about **non-metals**.

giant	density	lattice	weak	lost	charged	electrons	covalent

Unlike metals, non-metals tend to have a dull appearance and low ....

Non-metal atoms make .... bonds with each other by sharing

.... Many non-metals form small molecules with ....

forces of attraction between the molecules. Others form .... structures.

The atoms are arranged in a regular .... and have much stronger bonds.

Compounds between metals and non-metals contain ionic bonds, where the atoms have

gained or .... electrons to form .... particles,

which are strongly attracted to each other.

Q5 Draw lines to match the **properties** of non-metals on the left with their **causes** on the right.

Small molecules tend to have a low melting point.

Non-metal compounds do not conduct electricity.

Giant covalent structures have a high melting point.

There are strong bonds between the atoms.

Covalent compounds do not have free electrons.

There are weak forces of attraction between the molecules.

Q6 Ahmed is a materials scientist investigating four **non-metal compounds** with different properties. **Sodium chloride** and **magnesium chloride** are used in cooking, while **silicon tetrachloride** and **phosphorus trichloride** are highly toxic industrial chemicals.

a) Explain why the chlorides of silicon and phosphorus have low melting points. Use the information in the table to help you.

....

....

Name	Structure	Melting Point / °C
Sodium chloride	Giant ionic	801
Magnesium chloride	Giant ionic	714
Silicon tetrachloride	Small covalent	-70
Phosphorus trichloride	Small covalent	-112

b) Silica (silicon dioxide) has a melting point of 1710 °C. Explain why silica has such a high melting point.

....

....

Remember — silica has a giant covalent structure.

c) Ammonia (NH_3) has a melting point of -74 °C. Is its structure small or giant? ....

Checklist: Symbols and Formulas

Q1　Mr Federico is a **jeweller**. The diagrams below show two **rings** he has designed, and the **elements** they contain.

Write the symbol for each of the elements in the boxes on the diagram.

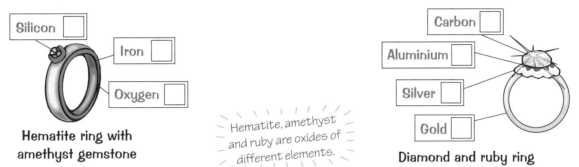

Silicon ☐
Iron ☐
Oxygen ☐

Hematite ring with amethyst gemstone

Hematite, amethyst and ruby are oxides of different elements.

Carbon ☐
Aluminium ☐
Silver ☐
Gold ☐

Diamond and ruby ring

Q2　Laurence has a part-time job helping Professor Bumble in his **laboratory**. The professor asks Laurence to collect some **chemicals** from the store cupboard, but Laurence spills his coffee over the **list** before he gets there.

Complete the table with the missing parts from Professor Bumble's list.

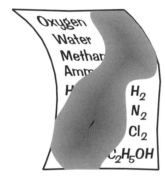

Oxygen
Water
Methan
Amm
H
H_2
N_2
Cl_2
C_2H_5OH

Molecule	Formula
Oxygen	
Water	
Methane	
Ammonia	
	H_2
	N_2
	Cl_2
	C_2H_5OH

Q3　Write the **formulas** for each of the compounds below.
　　　(The positive and negative ions have been given to help you.)

a)　silver chloride (Ag^+, Cl^-)　...

b)　calcium chloride (Ca^{2+}, Cl^-)　...

c)　water (H^+, O^{2-})　...

d)　magnesium oxide (Mg^{2+}, O^{2-})　...

e)　iron(II) bromide (Fe^{2+}, Br^-)　...

f)　lead(IV) oxide (Pb^{4+}, O^{2-})　...

g)　aluminium sulfide (Al^{3+}, S^{2-})　...

Formula 1

Limestone

Q1   Gary is a **builder**. He's teaching his apprentice, Kyle, about **limestone** and the different ways it can be used as a **building material**.

a)   Complete the following paragraph using words from the list below.

environmental	sea shells	quarrying
calcium carbonate	road surfacing	thousands

Limestone forms over .... of years from the remains

of things like .... Limestone is mainly made up of

.... It's extracted from the ground by

................................., which can cause some ....

problems. It's often used for making building blocks but can also be

crushed for use in .... Limestone can be

broken down into slaked lime.

b)   Kyle asks Gary how **slaked lime** (calcium hydroxide) is produced. Gary tells him that it's a two stage process. In the first stage limestone is **heated** to make **quicklime**.

i)   What is the chemical formula of limestone? Circle the correct answer.

CaO $CaCO_3$ CO_2 $Ca(OH)_2$

ii)   What **two** substances are produced when limestone is heated? Circle the correct answers.

CaO $CaCO_3$ CO_2 $Ca(OH)_2$

iii)   Gary tells Kyle that the reaction that takes place when limestone is heated is **endothermic**. Explain what is meant by the term endothermic reaction.

....

....

iv)   The next step in the production of slaked lime is to add **water** to quicklime. Write a **balanced** symbol equation for the formation of slaked lime.

....

Top Tips: It's been known for thousands of years that limestone is a dead useful building material. The Greeks used it to make sarcophaguses, Romans used to use it to build things like aqueducts and today we crush it up to make roads — bet those Romans are turning in their graves.

Limestone

Q2   Jane works for Sla-co, a company that produces **slaked lime** from **quicklime**.
Part of her job is to test the purity of quicklime before it's made into slaked lime.

   a)   She fills a beaker with water and records the temperature. She then adds a sample of
the quicklime and some universal indictor. Tick **two boxes** to show what she would observe.

The solution turns red.	☐
The solution turns blue.	☐
There is an increase in temperature.	☐
There is a decrease in temperature.	☐

Under acidic conditions Universal Indicator turns red, alkali conditions make it blue.

   b)   Is the reaction between quicklime and water an **exothermic** or **endothemic** reaction?

   ....

   c)   The majority of slaked lime produced by Sla-co is sold to farms.
Suggest a possible use for the slaked lime.

   ....

Q3   Limestone is an incredibly versatile building material. Complete the diagram to show the
different **products** that can be made using limestone and the **methods** used to produce them.

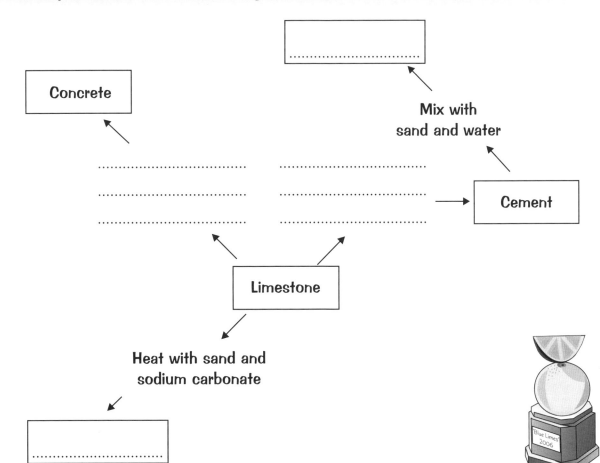

Limestone

Q4 The Keegan brothers run a **limestone quarry**.
The table on the right shows their annual spending.

Keegan Bros Quarry Annual expenditure	
Cost	**£ (thousands)**
Transport	20
Machinery	35
Electricity	1.5
Labour	63
After Quarrying Completion	
Total	131.5

a) Use the table to answer the questions below.

    i) How much is spent on 'After Quarrying Completion'? Circle the correct answer.

       £12 000   £20 000

            £15 000

    ii) What is the quarry's biggest expense?

    ....

    iii) What percentage of the total cost is spent on machinery?

    ....

b) Quarrying causes **environmental problems**.

    i) A large amount of energy is required to run the machinery used by the quarry.
Suggest a reason why high energy requirements could be bad for the environment.

    ....

    ....

    ii) Explain how transporting the limestone could damage the environment.

    ....

    ....

    iii) What effect does quarrying have on plants and animals in the surrounding area?

    ....

    ....

c) Profits from the quarry have been falling over recent years and so the Keegan brothers plan to close it. Give **two** potential disadvantages that closing the quarry might cause for the local town.

    1. ....

    2. ....

Top Tips:
For the exam don't just learn all the different uses of limestone and what it can be used to make, you also need to learn about all the environmental problems that quarrying it can cause. Things like noise pollution, unsightly tips, destruction of habitats and dust.

Metals and Alloys

Q1   Tick the boxes to show whether these statements are **true** or **false**.

<table>
<tr><td></td><td></td><td align="center">True</td><td align="center">False</td></tr>
<tr><td>a)</td><td>Steel is very malleable, this makes it ideal for water piping.</td><td align="center">☐</td><td align="center">☐</td></tr>
<tr><td>b)</td><td>Aluminium's resistance to corrosion makes it ideal for use outdoors.</td><td align="center">☐</td><td align="center">☐</td></tr>
<tr><td>c)</td><td>It is always better to use pure metals rather than alloys.</td><td align="center">☐</td><td align="center">☐</td></tr>
<tr><td>d)</td><td>Lead is used for flashing on roofs because it's malleable.</td><td align="center">☐</td><td align="center">☐</td></tr>
</table>

Q2   For his science homework Joshua has to identify different objects around his home and say whether they are made from **pure metals** or **alloys**. Complete the table below to show which are pure metals and which are alloys by putting ticks in the correct column.

Metal	Found in	Pure metal	Alloy
Brass	Door handles		✓
Lead	Flashing		
Copper	Water pipes		
Steel	Girders		
Solder	Electrical wiring		
Aluminium	Window frames		

Lead is often found on roofs, flashing around chimneys.

Q3   Malcolm is an **architect**. The different projects he works on require different materials with different **properties**. Use words from the list below to complete the paragraph about the properties of different **metals** and **alloys**.

copper	lead	protected	solder
steel	flexibility	rust	strength

Some metals like steel have great ...., which makes them

ideal for support structures like roof beams. For some purposes it is important to

use a metal or alloy that is soft and malleable, e.g. ....:

All metals conduct electricity, but .... is an exceptionally

good conductor so it's often used for electrical wiring. Iron and steel are cheap

but they .... if they are not protected.

Metals and Alloys

Q4 Hector works for a **builders' merchant**. They supply various metals and alloys in different sizes, shapes and lengths. The table shows six of the materials available and some of their **properties**.

Metal	Density (g/cm³)	Melting point (°C)	Malleability	Resistance to corrosion	Strength	Other comments
Steel	7.8	1430	Poor	Poor	Excellent	Very cheap
Solder	9.4	370	Good	Good	Poor	—
Aluminium	2.7	660	Poor	Excellent	Good	—
Lead	11.3	327	Excellent	Good	Poor	Dull, grey colour, toxic
Copper	8.9	1085	Good	Excellent	Average	Excellent conductor
Brass	8.4	940	Good	Good	Average	Shiny, decorative

Use the information in the table to answer the following questions.

a) One customer comes into the shop and asks for some **steel** to make a new **window frame**. Give a reason why steel would **not** be a good choice of material to make window frames.

....

b) The builders merchant's used to sell large quantities of **lead** however sales have declined over the years.

  i) Give one reason why we don't use lead to make fittings such as door handles and taps.

  ....

  ii) Most **water pipes** used to be made from lead. Suggest two reasons why lead was thought to be a good metal for this use.

  1. ....

  2. ....

  iii) Today most water pipes are made from **copper**. Suggest one reason why it is better to make water pipes from copper than lead.

  ....

c) The builders' merchants supply **aluminium** to a company that produces small wind turbines that can be attached to a roof to generate electricity. Give two reasons why aluminium is a good choice of material for this use.

  1. ....

  2. ....

Metals and Alloys

Q5   Harry and Alice were investigating whether a **new alloy** would be suitable for use **outdoors**.

They both immersed a piece of the alloy and four other substances (aluminium, steel, copper and brass) in **weak acid** for one week to simulate the corrosive effects of rainwater.
Harry and Alice set up their experiments as shown below.

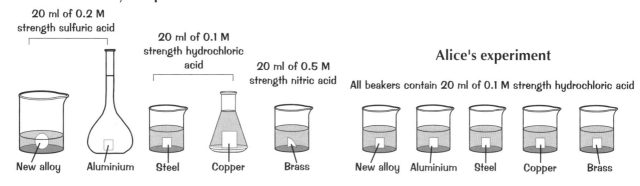

a)   Give one safety precaution that they should have taken during their experiments.

....

b)   Give two reasons why Alice's results are likely to be more reliable than Harry's.

1. ....

2. ....

c)   Which of the four named substances would you expect to corrode the most?

....

Q6   Jim is repairing a loose connection in his **radio**.

a)   The wires in the radio are made from **copper**. Give two reasons why copper is an ideal material to make electrical wires from.

1. ....

2. ....

b)   He is repairing the connection using **solder** and a soldering iron.
What property makes solder a good material for joining wires?

....

Top Tips: You may well be wondering what that top question has to do with materials for construction, well... in the exam they could ask you a question on health and safety or experimental design or both. Sneaky. Just learn the basics then apply it to the situation at hand.

<u>Polymers</u>

Q1 **Polymers** have many **uses** in the modern world. Complete the passage about polymers and some of their uses using words from the box.

| electricity | poor | dense | shopping bags |
| insulators | good | rigid | heat |

Some polymers, e.g. polyethene, are very flexible. This property makes them good for .... and squeezy bottles. Polyethene wouldn't be suitable for making car bumpers though, a more .... polymer like polypropene is often used. Most polymers are .... conductors of .... and .... Because polymers are good .... they're often used to make casings for electrical appliances.

Q2 A **chair designer** is researching different polymers that could be used to make a new range of **chairs**.

Polymer	Flexibility
Polyethene	Very flexible
Polypropene	Not flexible, very rigid
PVC	Stretchy and rigid

a) Why would the designer not want to make chairs out of polyethene?

....

b) Which polymer should the designer pick? Explain your choice.

....

Q3 Gladys sees an advert for a **frying pan** in a magazine. The pan's handle is made from a **polymer**.

a) Suggest one advantage of making the handle of a frying pan from a polymer.

....

b) Suggest one reason why the base of the frying pan is not made from a polymer.

....

Polymers

Q4   Felicity is a **material scientist** working for a company that produces a range of kitchen appliances and accessories. Complete the table by describing one **property** that the polymer used to make each object would need to have.

We are living in a material world and I am a material scientist.

Use of polymer	Property the polymer would need
Spatula	
Work surface	
Kettle casing	
Insulation around the kettle's electrical lead	

Q5   Jacques is a **polymer scientist** working with the European Space Agency. He is currently trying to develop a polymer to be used in the **protective casing** of a probe that will land on the planet Mercury before returning to Earth.

Jacques will need to take the following information into account when designing the polymer:

> • On re-entry to the Earth's atmosphere the probe might get struck by lightning.
>
> • The planet Mercury has an average surface temperature of 350 °C during the day and -170 °C during the night.

Non!

Suggest two properties that this new polymer will need.

1. ....

2. ....

Q6   **PTFE** is a polymer used to coat the surface of things like **frying pans** in order to make them **non-stick**. What properties should PTFE have? Circle the correct answer(s).

low melting point   high melting point   poor conductor of heat   non-toxic   good electrical conductor

Polymers

Q7 Mark works in the **research and development** department of a large **electronics company**. He is currently looking into new materials from which to make the casing of a **laptop** computer from. The table below shows some of the **properties** of four new polymers he could use.

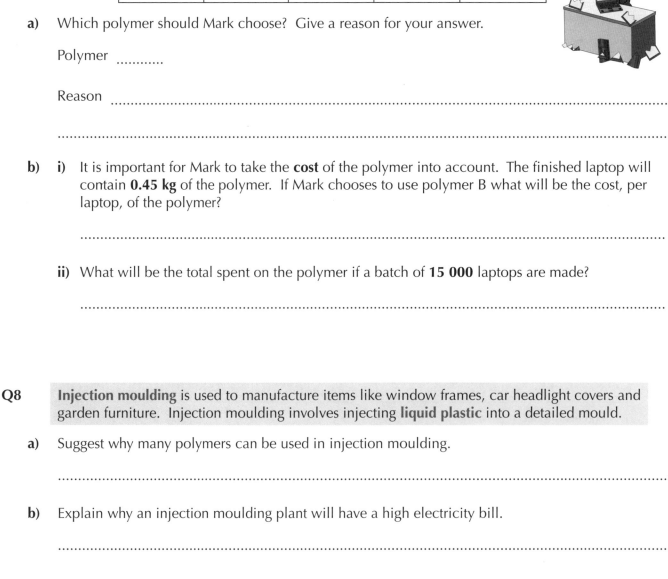

Polymer	Density (g/cm³)	Strength	Flexibility	Price (£/kg)
A	0.65	Poor	Poor	0.15
B	1.37	Excellent	Poor	0.75
C	0.95	Good	Poor	0.35
D	0.85	Good	Average	1.27

a) Which polymer should Mark choose? Give a reason for your answer.

Polymer ....

Reason ....

....

b) **i)** It is important for Mark to take the **cost** of the polymer into account. The finished laptop will contain **0.45 kg** of the polymer. If Mark chooses to use polymer B what will be the cost, per laptop, of the polymer?

....

ii) What will be the total spent on the polymer if a batch of **15 000** laptops are made?

....

Q8 **Injection moulding** is used to manufacture items like window frames, car headlight covers and garden furniture. Injection moulding involves injecting **liquid plastic** into a detailed mould.

a) Suggest why many polymers can be used in injection moulding.

....

b) Explain why an injection moulding plant will have a high electricity bill.

....

....

Ceramics

Q1 Draw lines to match each **ceramic** with the **material(s)** from which it is made.

glass

pottery and porcelain

cement

limestone and clay

sand and other chemicals

wet clay

Q2 Walter is a salesman in a shop that specialises in bathroom suites. He is discussing the possibility of a new **ceramic bathroom** with some customers.

a) Give **two** properties of ceramics that make them suitable for use in bathrooms.

1. ....

2. ....

b) Give **one** reason why a metal might be a better choice for bathroom fittings.

....

c) Why do you think some people still prefer ceramic to metal?

....

Q3 Ceramics are commonly used for a number of **fixtures and fittings** around the home. Put ticks in the boxes below to show why the objects listed are made from ceramics.

You can tick more than one box for each object.

	Hard wearing — it doesn't scratch easily	Waterproof and smooth — it's easily cleaned and hygienic	High melting point — it's fire resistant	Inert — it doesn't corrode
Porcelain toilet				
Ceramic kitchen sink				
Brick fire place				
Glass coffee table				

Top Tips: Ceramics are used for loads of different things and for good reason too — they're hard-wearing, waterproof, inert, have a high melting point and they're available in a whole range of pretty patterns and colours. The big downside is that they're brittle — they break fairly easily.

Ceramics

Q4 John is teaching an evening class about the different **ceramics** used in the building industry and how they can be **made**. Use words from the box to complete the passage below.

set	concrete	moulded	glazed	fired

When clay is wet it can be .... into any shape. If it is then ....

into pottery or porcelain it will keep its shape. It can then be .... to add

colours or patterns. Other well known ceramics include glass and cement. Cement

becomes runny when mixed with water. It will eventually .... and harden.

It can also be used to make ....

Q5 Scientists are constantly researching ways of making glass that is **tougher** and easier to **clean**.

Currently, plastics are cheaper than glass and break less easily.
Why do you think we still use glass for glazing rather than plastic?

....

....

What happens to plastic lab safety goggles over time? Are they easy to see out of?

Q6 Ben is designing a **TV** in his graphic design class. He'd like to use ceramics in his design.

a) Ben thought about using a ceramic like porcelain or pottery for the outer casing of the TV.

i) Give two advantages of using a ceramic for this purpose.

1. ....

2. ....

ii) Give one disadvantage of using a ceramic for this purpose.

....

b) Ben decided that his TV screen should be made out of glass.

i) Give two reasons why glass is suited to this use.

1. ....

2. ....

ii) Why do you think reinforced plastic is usually used instead of glass for hand-held TV screens?

....

Composites

Q1 Use the words below to complete the paragraph.

resin	flexibility	weight	regular	corrosion

Fibre reinforced composites have the strength of one component and the

.... of another. They have a good strength to

.... ratio. Most are also resistant to ....

Particle–based composites, as the name suggests, are mixtures of small

particles and .... These have a ....

structure, which makes them strong throughout.

Q2 SGT plastics produce **glass-reinforced plastic** (GRP). A material made of **plastic** reinforced with small fibres of **glass**. Customers can specify the ratio of glass to plastic depending on what they intend on using it for.

a) Give one advantage of using glass-reinforced plastic over ordinary plastic.

....

....

....

b) The table shows how the strength of GRP changes with the percentage of glass in the mixture.

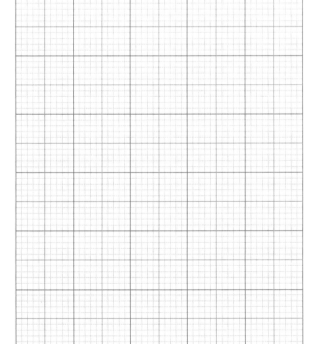

Percentage glass	Tensile strength (MPa)
20	132
40	160
60	205
80	245

i) Plot the data on the grid.

ii) Describe the trend in the graph you have drawn.

....

....

Choosing Materials for a Product

Q1 Construction engineers build "earthquake-proof buildings" in areas where earthquakes are likely. These buildings often have special features to help withstand an earthquake.

a) One of the materials that can be used to construct these buildings is reinforced concrete. What type of material is reinforced concrete an example of? Circle the correct answer.

ceramic   composite   polymer   alloy

b) Give **two** properties that you would expect reinforced concrete to have.

....

c) Why is reinforced concrete a good material to use for building in areas where earthquakes are likely?

....

....

Q2 Springsteen Building Supplies is a large builders' merchant. They supply a wide range of **materials** to the construction industry.

a) The table shows the annual percentage sales of materials from a builders merchants. Complete the table by calculating the percentage annual sales for iron.

Material	% of annual sales
Composites	22
Timber	33
Iron	
Steel	26

b) Give one **advantage** of using timber rather than iron or steel as a building material.

....

c) Give one **disadvantage** of using timber rather than iron or steel as a building material.

....

d) Some people in the industry predict that the amount of timber sold is likely to increase. Suggest a possible reason for this.

Metal isn't a renewable resource.

....

....

Choosing Materials for a Product

Q3 Tony is a **trainee draughtsman** for a leading **aircraft** manufacturer. He's learning about the different **materials** that could be used for making aeroplane **wings**.

a) Give one reason why each of the following would not be suitable for making aeroplane wings.

i) Steel ....

....

ii) Ceramics ....

....

b) What properties would the material used to make the wings need?

....

Q4 Anna has just bought a **listed building** that was built in 1672. Unfortunately over the years it has become a bit run down. Anna's about to begin the mammoth task of **renovating** it.

Because the building is listed she must use **traditional** alternatives to **modern** building materials.

a) The **window frames** need replacing. Anna cannot install plastic window frames, she must use wooden ones instead.

i) What are the advantages of using wood over plastic? Circle the correct answer(s).

there are more types   it's more in keeping
of wood than types   with the character   it provides   it's biodegradable
of plastic   of the house   better ventilation

ii) What are the advantages of using plastic over wood? Circle the correct answer(s).

it doesn't react
it's more   it can be painted   it's resistant   with the glass like
durable   any colour   to corrosion   wood does

b) Some of the **wooden panelling** inside the house also needs replacing. Give one advantage and one disadvantage of using plywood (the modern alternative) over wood panelling.

....

....

c) One of the **beams** needs replacing. Anna wanted to use steel but has been told that she must use wood. What would have been the advantage of using steel instead of wood for the beams?

....

The Home Environment   _Section 2.7 — Materials for Construction_

Choosing Materials for a Product

Q5 Ken is building a **garage** on the side of his house.
He has drawn up the following **design specification**.

- Strong and sturdy walls.
- Solid foundations.
- Waterproof and secure roof.
- Windows for workshop area at the rear.
- Secure entrance.

a) The garage needs to have a **roof**.

   i) Suggest a reason why **iron** would not be a suitable material for the roof.

   ....

   ii) Suggest a material that could be used for the roof.

   ....

b) Give one advantage of using **bricks** to build the walls of the garage.

....

c) To ensure the garage is secure Ken decided to use reinforced glass for the windows. Reinforced glass has a metal grate in it. What is the advantage of using a composite over ordinary glass?

....

d) i) Which of the following would be a suitable material for the **door handles**?
   Tick the correct box.

   Iron   ☐

   Wood   ☐

   Brass   ☐

   ii) Explain why you chose this material.

   ....

e) Ken used **concrete** for the foundations. Concrete is a mixture of cement, water, sand and gravel.
Give two reasons why concrete is well suited to this use.

   1. ....

   2. ....

Top Tips: As you may well have guessed, this section was all about being able to select the right materials for a job. Make sure you know about modern building materials and their advantages and disadvantages compared to traditional materials, like good old timber.

Energy in the Home

Q1 **Electrical appliances** convert **electricity** into **useful** forms of **energy**.

light energy	heat energy	kinetic energy	gravitational potential energy

a) From the list above, choose the forms of useful energy each of the following appliances converts electricity into.

i) Hairdryer ....

ii) Soldering iron ....

iii) Escalator ....

iv) Computer screen ....

v) Washing machine ....

b) Give another example of an appliance (not listed in part a) that converts electricity into each of the following forms of energy.

i) Light energy ....

ii) Heat energy ....

iii) Kinetic energy ....

iv) Gravitational potential energy ....

Q2 Helen has bought a new **house** near the centre of **town**. Choose a suitable **power source** for each of her appliances and give a reason for your choice.

a) Cooker:

i) Power source ....

ii) Reason for choice ....

....

b) Television:

i) Power source ....

ii) Reason for choice ....

....

Energy in the Home

Q3 Dave is an **energy consultant**. He's helping Claire compare all the different **energy sources** she could use in her home.

You can use words more than once.

Complete the following sentences using words from the list below.

expensive	natural	cheaper	portable	shocks	mains	electric
batteries	oil	electricity	less	impurities	gas	more	clean

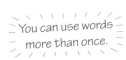

a) .... burns efficiently and

has few .... It is a .... fuel.

b) .... is available in bottles,

but is more .... than mains gas.

c) Because .... is a liquid it is easier to store than natural gas.

d) .... is very convenient and can

provide plenty of power, but is ....

e) Mains .... can be used for heating, lighting and powering

equipment containing motors.

f) .... from mains electricity could

kill you.

g) .... are safer than mains electricity, but they are

.... expensive.

h) .... are great for .... equipment

because you don't need to plug them into a mains socket.

Q4 Fred usually powers his **laptop computer** by plugging it into the mains electricity. He is considering buying a **battery** to power it instead.

Give one **advantage** and one **disadvantage** of using a battery to power a laptop.

Advantage: ....

Disadvantage: ....

Top Tips: Make sure you know your batteries from your plug sockets and your oil from your gas. It's useful to be able to weigh up which power sources would be most useful for different things.

Electrical Appliances

Q1   James is writing about **electrical appliances** for his homework.
Tick the boxes to show whether each of his statements is **true** or **false**.

True   False

a)   Switching a kettle on completes an electrical circuit and allows a current to flow. ☐ ☐

b)   Voltage flows through an appliance when it is switched on. ☐ ☐

c)   When an appliance is plugged into a wall socket, all three pins of the plug
are connected to the house's electrical supply. ☐ ☐

d)   Current is 'pushed' around a circuit by the power supply. ☐ ☐

Q2   Martin wants to know what the **electrical information**
on the sticker on the back of his computer means.

Draw lines to match the electrical quantities to their correct symbols and units.

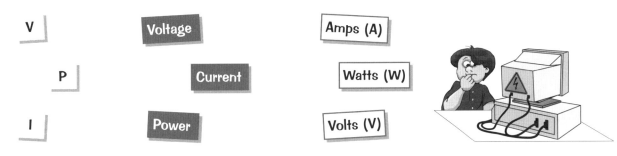

V	Voltage	Amps (A)
P	Current	Watts (W)
I	Power	Volts (V)

Q3   Robert has a number of **electrical components** and is not sure of their
power ratings. He tests each of the components, using an appropriate
power supply for each one. He designs a table to record the results.

You need to learn the formula for power.

Complete the table by calculating the power of each component.

Component	Voltage	Current	Power
Microphone 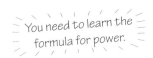	12	10	
Lamp	12	2	
Buzzer	230	6	
Motor	230	3.2	

Electrical Safety

Q1 George is an **electrical safety officer**. He is visiting a school to talk to the children about the **wiring** in electrical plugs and how it can help prevent **electric shocks**.

Complete the passage below by choosing from the words provided.

earth   live   three   ground   metal   electric shock   neutral   insulation   exposed

There are .... wires in a domestic plug, each coated in plastic

.... When an appliance is working properly, current only flows

through the .... and .... wires. If there's

a fault and the live wire touches any exposed .... parts of an

appliance, anyone touching that part could get an ....

To help prevent this, the .... wire is connected to the

.... metal parts of the appliance.

Q2 Pete the **electrician** is at Mrs Miggins' Pasty Shop. Her old metal electric kettle isn't working. Pete discovers the kettle's **fuse** has 'blown'.

a) Which wire in the kettle's plug is the fuse connected to?

....

b) Number the statements below to explain what happened to Mrs Miggins' kettle and the fuse.

☐ The kettle was safe again.

☐ The current was too high and the material inside the fuse started to heat up.

☐ A fault occurred in the kettle and the metal body became live and dangerous.

☐ The material in the fuse became very hot and melted.

☐ A large current flowed in the live and earth wires.

☐ The electrical supply was cut off.

Top Tips: Fuses work because they are part of the circuit. If the fuse 'blows' then the circuit is broken and no current can flow. The appliance is completely cut off from the mains supply.

Electrical Safety

Q3 Craig works as an **electrical safety consultant** and he has been asked to carry out a **risk assessment** of the kitchen at a local café.

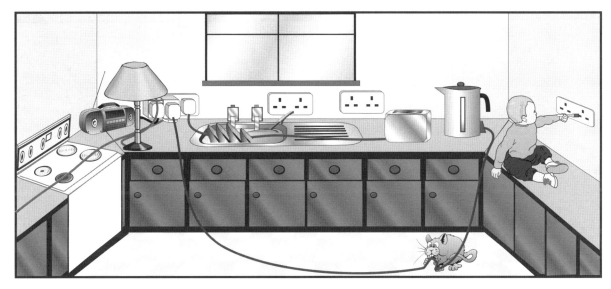

a) Look at the picture of the kitchen. There are at least **six** electrical hazards in the kitchen. List six of the ones you can spot.

1. ....

2. ....

3. ....

4. ....

5. ....

6. ....

b) Craig has completed the first stage of the risk assessment. What are the remaining four steps he must carry out to complete the risk assessment?

1. Look for hazards.

2. ....

3. ....

4. ....

5. ....

A café can be a very dangerous place.

c) Craig gives the café owner a poster showing what to do if someone gets an electric shock. Suggest **one** piece of advice the poster might give.

....

Electrical Safety

Q4 Gary bought a new **electric heater**. The first time he switched the heater on the **fuse blew**. Gary suspects that the **fuse** was the wrong **rating**.

a) The label on the heater says the power rating is **2 kW** and you know that the mains supply voltage is **230 V**. What is the **current** being drawn by the heater?

....

....

Don't forget the handy formula triangle and power needs to be in watts not kW.

b) The local hardware shop stocks 3 A, 5 A, 10 A and 13 A fuses.

i) Which fuse should Gary choose for the heater? ....

ii) Explain why he should choose this fuse.

....

....

c) Gary decides he ought to check that various appliances in his home have the correct fuse fitted. Work out the current drawn by each item when it's connected to the mains, and recommend the best fuse to use.

Appliance	Power	Current	Fuse
Hair straighteners	60 W	0.3 A	3 A
Popcorn maker	1.2 kW		
Kettle	2.4 kW		
Hairdryer	1.3 kW		

Q5 Tess is vacuuming her living room and the vacuum stops working. She tries it in some other sockets but none on the downstairs floor appear to be working. Tess decides to check the **circuit breakers**.

a) Briefly describe how a circuit breaker works.

....

....

....

b) What advantage do circuit breakers have over fuses?

....

Calculating Energy Usage and Cost

Q1 Terry is an **electrical appliance designer**. Below are some **household appliances** he has designed and their **power ratings**.

a) Number the appliances in order of how quickly they convert electrical energy into other forms of energy, starting with the one that converts energy the **fastest**.

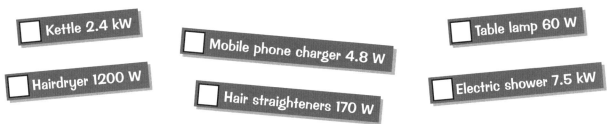

Kettle 2.4 kW

Mobile phone charger 4.8 W

Table lamp 60 W

Hairdryer 1200 W

Hair straighteners 170 W

Electric shower 7.5 kW

b) How much electrical energy do the hair straighteners convert into other forms of energy each second?

....

Q2 Using the formula P = E ÷ t, calculate the **power** of the following **appliances**.

Don't forget energy is in joules and time is in seconds.

a) A **radio** that converts 40 J of energy into heat and sound energy in 2 seconds.

....

b) An **electric blender** that converts 18 kJ of energy into kinetic, heat and sound energy in 1 minute.

....

c) A **toaster** that converts 153 kJ of energy into heat energy in 90 seconds.

....

Q3 Richard thinks that he is using too much **electricity** in his home and that his electricity bill will be very **expensive**. He draws a table to help him work out if he is right.

Appliance	Power	Time left on	Energy used (kWh)	Cost (p)
Electric heater	2 kW	3 hours	6	120
Travel iron	1.2 kW	0.5 hours		
Surround sound hi-fi	500 W	1 hour 30 minutes		
Light bulb	60 W	3 hours 15 minutes		

a) Calculate the electrical energy used by each appliance. The first one has been done for you.

b) The Wattless Electricity Company charges **20p per kWh**. Complete the table by calculating how much each appliance costs to run for the time given. The first one has been done for you.

Using Energy Efficiently

Q1   Sophie wants to know what type of **energy** her appliances **waste** energy as.

Draw lines to connect the **output** energy arrows with the correct **energy** type(s).

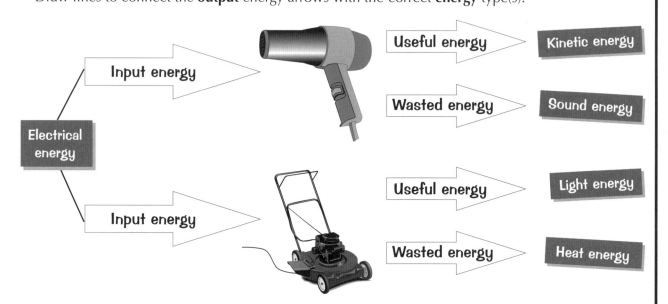

Electrical energy

Input energy

Useful energy — Kinetic energy

Wasted energy — Sound energy

Input energy

Useful energy — Light energy

Wasted energy — Heat energy

Q2   Kaitlin is shopping for a new **fridge** and is keen to buy an **efficient** one. The shop assistant at Fridge Universe tells her, wrongly, that the more efficient the fridge, the **colder** it keeps your food.

Fill in the gaps in the following passage using words from the box to explain what is really meant by the efficiency of an appliance. You can use words more than once.

| efficient | sound | hot | better | input | wasted | noise |
| electrical | used | heat | converting | useful | energy | |

Electrical appliances have an .... of ....
energy. Not all of this is converted into .... energy. Some of
the energy is .... This energy does not disappear — it is still
there but in forms which can't be easily .... Energy is often
wasted as .... or .... energy. The
.... an appliance is at .... the input
energy into useful energy, the more .... it is said to be.

Using Energy Efficiently

Q3 Mark has designed three **lawn mowers**. He wants to know which one is more **efficient**. The table shows how much energy is converted into **useful** energy or **wasted** for each lawn mower.

Lawn mower	Input energy (J)	Useful output energy (J)	Wasted output energy (J)	Efficiency (%)
1	200	160		
2	550		130	
3		900	345	

a) Fill in the missing energy figures in the table.

b) Calculate the efficiency of each device, using the formula:

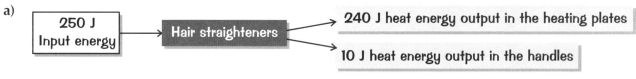

$$\text{Efficiency} = \frac{\text{Useful output energy}}{\text{Input energy}} \times 100\%$$

Q4 For a school project, Ashley is given the **input** and **output** energies for certain household appliances and must calculate the **efficiency** of each device. For each of the appliances below, circle the **useful** energy output(s), and calculate the **efficiency** of each device.

a)

250 J Input energy	→	**Hair straighteners**	→	240 J heat energy output in the heating plates
			→	10 J heat energy output in the handles

Efficiency = ...

b)

550 J Input energy	→	**Filament lamp**	→	44 J output light energy
			→	506 J output heat energy

Efficiency = ...

c)

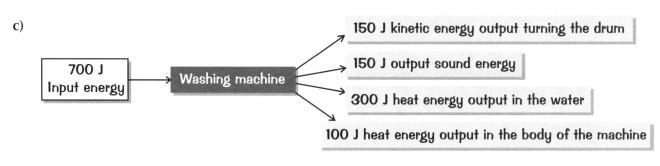

700 J Input energy	→	**Washing machine**	→	150 J kinetic energy output turning the drum
			→	150 J output sound energy
			→	300 J heat energy output in the water
			→	100 J heat energy output in the body of the machine

Efficiency = ...

Top Tips: Efficiency is one of those rare topics in physics that makes sense — if you put loads of energy into a machine, but get little useful energy out in return, your machine isn't efficient. Easy.

Using Energy Efficiently

Q5 The filament lamp in Tim's bedside light has blown. He's trying to decide
whether to buy a **low-energy lamp** or an ordinary **filament lamp** to replace it.
The shop assistant shows Tim the following information.

Type of lamp	Cost to buy	Lifetime of lamp (h)	Power (kW)
Filament lamp	50p	1000	0.06
Low-energy lamp	£5	11 000	0.015

a) How many filament lamps would you need to buy to last as long as **one** low-energy lamp?

....

b) How much would it cost to buy this number of filament lamps? ....

c) Tim pays **18p per kWh** for electricity. Calculate the cost of using each type of lamp for
11 000 hours.

i) Filament lamp: ....

ii) Low-energy lamp: ....

d) What is the **total cost** (purchase plus electricity cost) of running each lamp for 11 000 hours?

i) Filament lamp: ....

ii) Low-energy lamp: ....

e) Suggest **one** advantage, other than saving money, of using low-energy instead of filament lamp.

....

Q6 Modern appliances such as fridges and dishwashers are labelled according to how
efficient they are. The energy ratings go from **A (most efficient)** to **G (least efficient)**.

a) Complete the table below about the efficiency of four freezers.

Model	Energy rating	Cost to buy (£)	Running cost per year (£)	Running cost for 5 years (£)	Total cost to buy and run for 1 year (£)	Total cost to buy and run for 5 years (£)
Coldpoint 23	B	350	30			
Coldpoint X6	A	340	13			
Twirlpool 31	E	240	80			
Twirlpool 99	C	230	55			

b) Which freezer is cheapest to buy and run:

i) Over **one** year? ....   **ii)** Over **five** years? ....

Heat Transfer

Q1   Max wants to know which type of **heat transfer** occurs in which situations. Complete the table by putting a tick in the correct column(s) to match each property to the type of heat transfer. A property can apply to more than one type of heat transfer.

		Thermal radiation	Conduction	Convection
a)	Only occurs in liquids and gases			
b)	How we feel heat from the Sun			
c)	Occurs in solids, liquids and gases			
d)	Vibrating particles pass their energy to their neighbours			
e)	Higher energy particles in the hotter region move to the cooler region			
f)	Occurs mainly in solids			

Q2   **Heat transfer** to or from an **object** depends on its temperature and the **temperature** of its **surroundings**.

a) Calculate the temperature difference between the following objects and their surroundings.

    A Hot kettle: temperature is 100 °C, temperature of surroundings is 21 °C ....

    B Soldering iron tip: temperature is 280 °C, temperature of surroundings is 22 °C ....

    C Snowman: temperature is –1 °C, temperature of surroundings is 4 °C ....

b) Put the objects, A-C, in part a) in order according to how quickly heat is transferred to or from the surroundings. Start with the slowest.

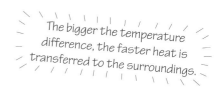

The bigger the temperature difference, the faster heat is transferred to the surroundings.

    ....,' ....,' ....

Q3   Simon is doing a project on **heat transfer in the home**. Help him out by explaining how heat is transferred in each of the following situations.

a) How heat is transferred from the electric ring on the hob to milk in a pan on top of it.

    ....

    ....

b) How heat is transferred from the Sun to the air inside a greenhouse.

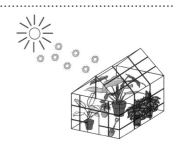

    ....

    ....

Heat Transfer

Q4   **Thermal imaging cameras** can be used to detect objects which are warmer than their surroundings. They work by detecting the **infrared radiation** emitted by objects — the hotter the area, the brighter it will appear.

Explain how thermal imaging cameras can be used by the following people at work.

a)   Police helicopter units following a suspected burglar through a housing estate at night.

....

....

b)   An energy efficiency consultant doing a heat loss survey on the outside of a house.

....

....

Q5   Circle the statement from each pair below which will **increase** thermal radiation from an object.

a)   **Making the surface smooth with no folds and bumps.** / Adding 'fins' to increase the surface area.

b)   **Painting it with white radiator paint.** / Painting it black.

c)   **Painting it with a matt green paint.** / Painting it with a gloss paint in the same colour.

Q6   Electronic components (e.g. computer processors) often generate a lot of **heat**. Many components have **heat sinks** fitted to them to help keep them cool.

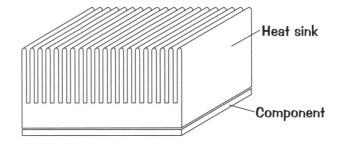

Heat sinks are usually made of metal and have lots of 'fins'.
Explain why this design is a good one to help cool the component.

....

....

Top Tips: Remember, **convection** only happens in **fluids** (liquids and gases), **conduction** happens fastest in **solids**, but **all** objects emit and absorb heat **radiation**.

Heat Transfer

Q7   Inga is investigating **thermal radiation**. She fills three coloured mugs with boiling water and feels which is radiating the **most** heat by holding her hand close to each one, without touching it.

a)   Inga has the following coloured mugs: **shiny white**, **matt black** and **shiny black**.
Arrange the mugs in order from the one that radiates the most heat to the one that radiates the least.

....

b)   Inga's experiment is not very scientific. Suggest **one** way Inga could improve her experiment.

....

Q8   A **lava lamp** is made up of a base containing an **electric bulb**, with a glass bottle sitting on top of it. The bottle contains **wax** and a transparent **oil**.

Number the sentences below to describe how the lava lamp works.
Assume the lamp has been on for some time and all the wax has melted.

☐ This causes the wax to expand and become less dense than the oil. The wax begins to rise.

☐ As the wax rises towards the top of the lamp, it cools and becomes denser than the oil. The wax sinks.

☐ A 'blob' of molten wax near the light bulb is heated through convection.

☐ As the wax nears the base of the lamp, it is re-heated by the light bulb and the process starts again.

Oil — Wax

Lightbulb

Base

Q9   Janek is designing a range of **cookware**. He is choosing materials for a frying pan set. He has found the following information from **material data** sheets.

Material	Melting point	Thermal conductivity
Wood	Not applicable	Poor
Aluminium	660 °C	Very good
Polymer	Softens around 100 °C	Poor
Steel	1420 °C	Good

Chocolate frying pans
never really took off

Using this information, choose a suitable material for the following:

a)   The frying pan body. ....

b)   The frying pan handle. ....

c)   A heat-resistant mat to protect the worktop. ....

Heat Transfer in the Home

Q1 Don is thinking about fitting **loft insulation**. The information leaflet in Energy Planet World says that he will save around **£60 per year** on his heating bill if he does. The insulation will **cost £240**.

What is the payback time of the loft insulation?

....

Q2 Mrs Diggles is interested in improving the energy **efficiency** of the flat where she lives.

a) Calculate the payback time for the improvements shown in the table.

Improvement	Initial cost	Annual saving	Payback time (years)
Double glazing	£1500	£50	
Hot-water tank jacket	£10	£15	
Draught proofing	£40	£40	
Loft insulation	£210	£70	

b) Mrs Diggles plans to move out of the flat in 10 months time.
Which improvement would you recommend? Give a reason for your answer.

....

....

Q3 Enid the **energy consultant** is on her way to work in the snow. She spots this house on the way.

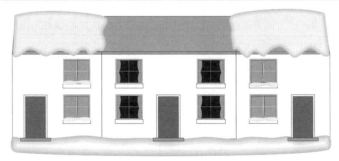

Enid thinks the house could do with an energy survey.

a) Why does she think the house could be losing a lot of heat?

....

b) Suggest **one** step the owner could take to reduce the heat loss.

....

Heat Transfer in the Home

Q4 Jake is having a **new house** built. The designer is explaining ways that he can **reduce heat loss**. Draw lines to match the following ways to reduce heat loss from the home with their correct descriptions.

Hot water tank jacket

Draught proofing

Central heating room thermostat

Loft insulation

Double glazing

Cavity wall insulation

Each window has two layers of glass instead of one

Foam is installed in the gap between the inner and outer layer of bricks

A thick layer of fibreglass is laid out across the whole loft floor

A thick insulating material is wrapped around the hot water tank

Gaps around doors, windows and floors are plugged with foam, plastic or paper

Switches the heating off when the inside of the house reaches a set temperature and back on when the temperature drops

Q5 To try and encourage people to insulate their homes, the Government have made grants available to some people to help pay for **insulation**. Energy Planet World has produced another handy information leaflet giving typical **prices** and estimated **savings** for various types of houses.

Type of house	Full price of insulation	Grant (if eligible)	Estimated saving per year
2 bed end terrace	£300	£50	£50
3 bed semi-detached	£375	£75	£60
4 bed semi-detached	£455	£125	£80

a) Mary wants to reduce her heating bills. She lives in a three-bed semi detached house and is eligible for a grant. What is the payback time if she installs cavity wall insulation?

....

b) Describe how cavity wall insulation reduces the amount of heat lost from a house.

....

....

Useful Mixtures in the Home

Q1 For each of the following mixtures, **circle** the **solvent** and **underline** the **solute**.

a) A solution of colouring in ethanol.

b) A cup of tea made with boiling water and one sugar.

c) Salt water from the sea.

d) Chlorine in swimming pool water.

e) Carbon dioxide in fizzy water.

Q2 Lynn leaves a glass of **tap water** on a sunny windowsill. A few days later she notices that the water level has **dropped** and there is a **dirty ring** on the glass where the water was.

Complete the following passage by choosing words from the box to fill in the gaps.

solids	solution	melted	dissolved	evaporated	liquids	condensed	solute

The water level has dropped because some of the water has .... in the warmth from the Sun. Tap water is not pure, but is a .... with a lot of substances .... in it. Some of these were left behind as .... on the surface of the glass as the water level dropped.

Q3 Bob wants to carry out an experiment to investigate the **evaporation rate** of a solvent from a solution. Which **container** would be the best one to use for this? Circle the correct answer.

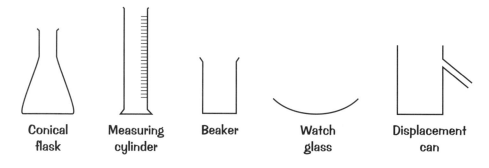

| Conical flask | Measuring cylinder | Beaker | Watch glass | Displacement can |

Q4 **Perfume** is a solution of scented oils dissolved in a **solvent**.

a) Name **one** solvent that is often used in perfume. ....

b) What happens to the solvent when perfume is applied to the skin?

....

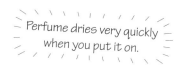

Perfume dries very quickly when you put it on.

Useful Mixtures in the Home

Q5 When **chemists** design new products they choose the **type of mixture** according to what the product will be **used** for. Complete the following sentences using words from the box, to describe three common uses of mixtures.

hair gel	suspension	dries	condenses	aerosol		spray paint		solution
emulsion	foam	evaporates		nail varnish	solute	solvent	gel	sets

a) .... is a .... that can be easily applied as a liquid.

When applied, the .... in it evaporates to leave coloured particles behind.

b) .... is a .... with the right consistency to create a

hairstyle. It also .... quickly to hold the style in place.

c) .... is an .... that is easy to apply in an even,

thin layer over a large area and .... very quickly.

Q6 Tracey is thinking about what **solvents** she might need when she is **decorating**. The table give some properties of various paint solvents.

Solvent	Will dissolve...	Won't dissolve...	Toxicity	Volatility	Effect on environment
Water	Wet emulsion paint	Gloss paint	Non-toxic	-	-
White spirit	Wet gloss paint	Dry paint	Toxic	Quite volatile, creates fumes	Harmful
Dichloromethane	Almost all household paint and varnish, wet or dry	-	Very toxic, corrosive (burns skin)	Very volatile, creates a lot of fumes	Harmful

a) What solvent would be best for Tracey to use for the following jobs?

i) Stripping the old paint from the woodwork. ....

ii) Cleaning paint brushes after glossing the woodwork. ....

iii) Cleaning equipment after painting the walls with emulsion paint. ....

b) Suggest **two** health and safety precautions Tracey should take when she is using the toxic solvents.

....

....

Useful Mixtures in the Home

Q7 Tick the boxes to show whether the following statements are **true** or **false**.

		True	False
a)	An aerosol is a liquid dispersed in another liquid.	☐	☐
b)	A foam contains tiny droplets of liquid.	☐	☐
c)	A foam can be made of a solid or a liquid but it always has gas bubbles dispersed in it.	☐	☐
d)	Foams and aerosols both contain tiny gas bubbles.	☐	☐
e)	Aerosols contain droplets of liquid dispersed in a gas.	☐	☐
f)	A foam is always made from a solid.	☐	☐

Q8 Kiran has prepared some mixtures for testing. Unfortunately he has to leave them for half an hour and when he comes back, some of them look different. Use the before and after pictures below to decide what **type of mixtures** they could be.

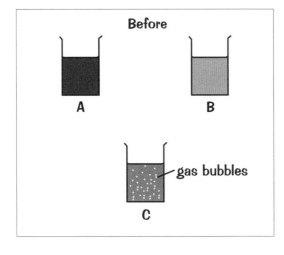
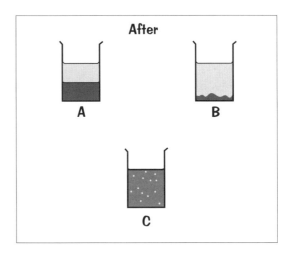

A ....

B ....

C ....

Q9 Vincent wants to repaint his house. He finds some **paint** left over from the last time, but when he opens it he discovers a layer of thin **clear liquid on top**.

a) What sort of paint is he using?

....

b) Suggest **one** type of solvent that is often used in paint.

....

Mixed Questions for Sections 2.6-2.8

Q1   Limestone is **quarried** from the surface of the Earth. It can be used in
its raw form to **build houses** or used to make other **building materials**.

   a) **i)** Write a symbol equation to show what happens when limestone is heated.

        ....

      ii) This reaction is **endothermic**. Explain what is meant by an endothermic reaction.

        ....

        ....

   b) Limestone can be heated with powdered clay to make **cement**.
Give one other building material that is made using limestone.

        ....

   c) **Iron** is also used as a building material.

      i) What is the chemical symbol for iron? ....

      ii) Give a property of iron that makes it suitable for its use as a construction material.

        ....

Q2   Paul is worried that he is not using energy **efficiently** in his home.

   a) Paul is considering changing his **filament lamps** to **low-energy lamps**.
Give **two** advantages and **two** disadvantages of using low-energy lamps.

     Advantages

     1. ....

     2. ....

     Disadvantages

     1. ....

     2. ....

   b) Paul thinks that he is losing a lot of heat from his home so he invests in draught-proofing,
loft insulation and double glazing. State which type(s) of heat transfer is limited by each
type of insulation.

      i) draught-proofing ....

      ii) loft insulation ....

      iii) double glazing ....

Mixed Questions for Sections 2.6-2.8

Q3 Jenny's **television** isn't working and needs a **new fuse**.

a) Describe how a fuse will make a television safe if a fault causes a surge in the current.

....

....

b) Jenny needs to know the current drawn by the television so that she can choose the right fuse. The supply to the television is 230 V and the power consumption is 80 W when it is on. Calculate the current.

....

c) Jenny has three fuses, a **5A**, a **10A** and a **13A** fuse. Which one should she use for the television?

....

d) What forms of energy does Jenny's television convert electrical energy into?

....

e) Jenny's electricity supplier charges **11p per kWh**. What is the cost of using her television for two hours?

....

....

Q4 Gemma is **cleaning** the **kitchen** after having some friends over for dinner.

a) She cleans the **ceramic** tiles with soap and water.

　i) Give **two** characteristic properties of ceramics.

　　1. ....

　　2. ....

　ii) What is the chemical formula for water? ....

b) Gemma then cleans the oven with a **foam oven cleaner**.

　i) Describe the composition of a foam.

　　..

　　..

　ii) The oven burns propane. Complete the symbol equation for the complete combustion of propane.

$$C_3H_8 + 5O_2 \rightarrow 3\text{.....................} + 4\text{.....................}$$

Mixed Questions for Sections 2.6-2.8

Q5   Jack is **designing** a **new house** for himself.

a)   He chooses to use **reinforced concrete** as one of the building materials.

   i)   What four materials make up normal concrete?

   ....

   ii)   Give one way in which reinforced concrete is better than normal concrete.

   ....

b)   Jack chooses to fit **plastic** window frames rather than traditional wooden ones.
Give one reason why Jack may have chosen to do this.

   ....

c)   Jack buys a new kettle for his house. The kettle is **metal** with a **plastic** handle.

   i)   Give two properties that the polymer used to make the handle will have.

   1. ....

   2. ....

   ii)   Why is it important that Jack's new kettle is earthed?

   ....

   ....

d)   The electrical wiring in Jack's house will be made of **copper**.
Explain why metals are good conductors of electricity.

   ....

   ....

   ....

e)   **Lead** will be used to waterproof the joints on the roof. What is the chemical symbol for lead?

   ....

f)   Jack decides that he wants the walls of his house to be painted blue. The paint he chooses is an emulsion. Describe the composition of an emulsion.

   ....

   ....

Section 2.9 — Transport

Speed

Q1   Joanna gets the bus to school every day. It takes her **300 s** to walk the **500 m** from her house to the bus stop.

    a)   What is Joanna's average speed during the walk to the bus stop?

    ....

    b)   The bus normally takes **15 minutes** to drive to school at an average speed of **10 m/s**. How far is the school from Joanna's bus stop?

    ....

Q2   Blankshire Council has installed a **speed camera** by the side of a road. When Sam's car passes **point A**, a timer in the camera starts. **Half a second** later the camera takes a picture of the car.

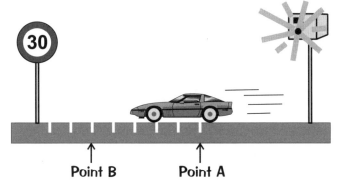

    a)   Sam's car travels a distance of **d** metres between point A and point B. Circle the formula that should be used to calculate the speed of Sam's car.

        speed $= d \div 5$ speed $= 5 \times d$ speed $= 0.5 \times d$ speed $= d \div 0.5$

    b)   Each of the white lines marked on the road are 2 m apart.

        i)   How far does Sam's car travel between point A and point B?

        ....

        ii)   Calculate the speed of the car.

        ....

        iii)   The speed limit is 30 mph, which is **13.4 m/s**. Was Sam breaking the speed limit?

        ....

Top Tips: Remember speed and velocity both measure how fast you're going — the only difference is that velocity has a direction too, e.g. 50 m/s is a speed, 50 m/s west is a velocity. Easy.

Acceleration

Q1 Fionda Cars are producing a new brochure for their range of cars. Complete the table to show the **time** it takes each car to accelerate from **0 to 27 m/s** (60 mph).

Model	Acceleration (m/s^2)	Time to reach 27 m/s (s)
Tiger	2.6	
Zephyr	2.8	
Monarch	5.0	

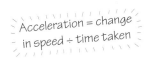

Acceleration = change in speed ÷ time taken

Q2 Jason accelerates from **16 m/s** along a sliproad to join the motorway **4 s** later at **30 m/s**. Calculate Jason's acceleration.

....

....

Q3 George is a **train engineer** and is writing a handbook for drivers of a new express train that can reach **36 m/s**. When the brakes are applied, the train decelerates at **0.12 m/s^2**. How many minutes before the train is due to stop should the driver begin **braking** if the train is travelling at **full speed**?

....

....

....

You know the final speed is 0 m/s (it has stopped) so you can find the change in speed.

Q4 Two teams are competing to see who has designed the **fastest jet car**. The cars, **Superflash** and **Speedyzoom**, are timed as they cross a **1 km** section of a straight track. The table below shows data collected by the judge.

Car	Initial speed (m/s)	Final speed (m/s)	Time taken (s)	Acceleration (m/s^2)
Superflash	95	345	20	
Speedyzoom	95		21	12

a) Complete the table.

b) Which team won the competition? Circle the correct answer.

Superflash   **Speedyzoom**

Cars and Stopping Distances

Q1   Carla is preparing a **driving safety leaflet** that contains a section on **stopping distances**.

a)   What is meant by 'braking distance'?

....

b)   Use the words in the box to complete the following word equations.

braking	speed	reaction time	thinking

i)   Thinking distance = ... × ....

ii)   Stopping distance = ... distance + ... distance

Q2   Simon is a **transport engineer** involved in designing the **brakes** for a new car.
He needs to know how each of the factors below affects **stopping distances**
to make the brakes as effective as possible. Tick the boxes next to each factor
to show if it affects **thinking distance** only, **braking distance** only or **both**.

Factor	Thinking distance only	Braking distance only	Both
Drugs or alcohol			
Tiredness			
Age			
Speed			
Mass of load			
Condition of brakes			
Condition of tyres			
Type of road surface			
Weather conditions			

Q3   Three **policemen** are trying to plan a road safety campaign. They know
the stopping distance for a typical car going **30 mph** in good conditions is
23 m. They are trying to work out the typical stopping distance at **60 mph**.

Stan says:

"60 mph is twice as fast, so a
car would go twice as far. The
stopping distance will double."

Matt says:

"The reaction time will be the same,
so thinking distance won't change.
The braking distance will double."

Alex says:

"The thinking distance will double, but the braking distance will more than double."

Who is right?

....

Cars and Stopping Distances

Q4 Anya manages a **motorway service station**. She calls a meeting to see what they can do to help improve **road safety**.

Services 1 m

Give a reason why each of the following suggestions might be a good idea.

a) Build a hotel next to the service station where people on long journeys could stay.

....

b) Stop selling alcohol anywhere in the service station. ....

....

c) Sell tyre tread gauges in the shop. ....

....

Q5 Laurence **drives to work** every morning. Read the description of one journey Laurence took last **winter**, then answer the questions below.

8:30 am Laurence sets off from his house in the town centre where the speed limit is 30 mph. It is a sunny but cold morning.

8:35 am Laurence picks up his friend Amy.

8:40 am Laurence joins an A-road where the speed limit is 50 mph, so increases his speed.

8:50 am Laurence turns into the road that leads to his work. The road is shaded by trees and there are patches of ice on the road.

8:55 am Laurence and Amy arrive at work.

a) **i)** What will happen to the stopping distance of Laurence's car after he picks up Amy? Circle the correct answer.

It will increase   It will decrease   It will stay the same

ii) Give a reason for your answer.

....

b) When Laurence increases his driving speed, the overall stopping distance of his car will increase. Why is this? Circle the correct answer.

Because the braking time will decrease.   Because the reaction time will increase.

Because the thinking distance and braking distance will increase.   Because the braking distance will increase.

Remember, braking distance is the distance travelled while the brakes are being applied.

c) Why will driving over ice increase Laurence's braking distance?

....

Transport Safety

Q1   Trevor is a **mechanic**. Part of his job is to give cars their annual MOT test.

Describe how having an MOT test:

a)   improves car safety.

....

b)   reduces the environmental impact of driving.

....

Q2   Mary has just passed her **driving test**.

a)   Why do learner drivers have to pass:

i)   a theory test?

....

ii)   a practical test?

....

b)   Mary has a hands free kit in her car so she can use her mobile phone.
Explain why it is dangerous to hold and use a mobile phone while driving.

....

Q3   The graph shows the number of people killed in **road accidents** in country X each year since **1985**.

a)   Approximately how many people were killed in road accidents in **1997**?

....

b)   Describe the trend in the number of road deaths between 1985 and 2005.

....

....

Deaths from road accidents in country X

c)   In **1990** a law was passed making it compulsory for people in the front of a car to wear a **seatbelt**. Did this have an effect on the number of road deaths? Give a reason for your answer.

....

....

Transport Safety

Q4   Jeremy is a **car designer** and is studying how **technology** can improve **car safety**.
Describe how each of the safety features below work.

a)   Crumple zones in the car bodywork

....

b)   Seatbelts

....

c)   Testing cars with crash test dummies

....

d)   Airbags

....

Q5   Tony is a **road safety officer**. He thinks the **speed limit** in the local
town should be reduced. He is analysing the results of a study into
how many **pedestrians survive** being hit by a car at **different speeds**.

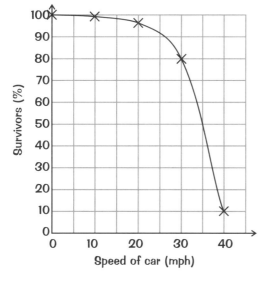

a)   What percentage of pedestrians survive
when hit by a car at **30 mph**?

....

b)   At what speed do 50% of pedestrians survive?

....

c)   What is the percentage of pedestrians who
are **killed** when hit by a car at 40 mph?

....

d)   How do drivers know what the speed limit is on a particular stretch of road?

....

e)   Why is the speed limit lowest in towns and villages, particularly near schools,
and highest on motorways?

....

Top Tips: It's true, travelling by car can be dangerous. New technology and driving laws
have increased car safety — but it's up to individual drivers to make sure they don't put others at risk.

Fuel for Transport

Q1 Trevor works on an **oil rig** in the North Sea, where they extract crude oil. Tick the boxes to show whether the following statements about crude oil are **true** or **false**.

True   False

a) Crude oil is a fossil fuel.

b) Crude oil is a renewable fuel.

c) Crude oil is used to produce nuclear power.

d) Crude oil is used to produce petrol and diesel.

e) Crude oil can be burnt.

f) Oil rigs extract crude oil from sea water.

True or false — crude oil makes a tasty salad dressing?

Q2 Crude oil contains a mixture of different **hydrocarbons**. These are **separated** to produce fuels like **petrol** and **diesel**.

a) What is a hydrocarbon?

....

b) The diagram on the right shows a molecule of a hydrocarbon used for fuel.

   i) Label one hydrogen atom and one carbon atom.

   ii) What is the chemical formula for this molecule?

   ....

c) Circle **all** of the compounds below that are hydrocarbons.

   CO_2 C_3H_8 C_2H_4 CO H_2O C_2H_5OH

Q3 Diesel contains stored **chemical energy**, which is released in a car **engine** to power the car.

a) How is the energy stored in diesel released? Circle the correct answer.

   burning   heating   melting   adding sulfur   taking oxygen away

b) Complete the balanced symbol equation for the combustion of a hydrocarbon.

   C_7H_{16} + ... $O_2 \rightarrow$ .... CO_2 + ... H_2O (+ energy)

   The balanced equation below shows the combustion of a different hydrocarbon.

   C_xH_y + 14 $O_2 \rightarrow$ 9 CO_2 + 10 H_2O (+ energy)

c) Use the pattern in hydrocarbon reactions to work out which hydrocarbon is being burnt. Circle the correct answer.

   C_5H_{12} C_6H_{14} C_7H_{16} C_9H_{20} C_4H_{10}

Fuel Efficiency and Energy Transfer

Q1 Richard is an **engineer** helping in the **design** of a new **engine**. He is studying the way **energy** is **converted** from one form to another in the engine of a car.

a) Complete the blanks in the paragraph.

When fuel is burned in the engine, ... energy is converted

to .... energy. The engine changes this into

.... energy, which can be transferred to make the car move.

b) None of the energy transfers are 100% efficient. Circle the statement that explains why.

Some energy is converted to a form that is not useful each time a transformation happens.

Some energy disappears each time a transformation happens.

Some energy is destroyed each time a transformation happens.

Q2 The two equations below show the **combustion** of petrol in a car engine.

$C_8H_{18} + 12½O_2 \rightarrow 8CO_2 + 9H_2O$ (+ energy)
$C_8H_{18} + 8O_2 \rightarrow 2CO_2 + 3CO + 3C + 9H_2O$ (+ energy)

a) Name the **two** extra products of incomplete combustion, compared to complete combustion.

....

b) Fill in the blanks in the following sentences.

Incomplete combustion happens when there is not enough ....
for complete combustion. It releases .... energy than complete combustion.

Q3 Jenny and Roger work for Froggart Cars. Jenny's team have designed a new, **more efficient** engine that **minimises** incomplete combustion. Roger, a salesman, is finding out about the new engine.

Draw lines to match up Roger's questions with Jenny's answers.

Why is incomplete combustion dangerous?

To make sure the engine is running as efficiently as possible.

The engine is not 100% efficient, so what happens to the energy that is not used?

It is mostly wasted as heat and spreads out into the atmosphere.

Why does the engine need to be serviced regularly?

It releases toxic pollutants into the air.

Alternative Fuels

Q1 Carlos works for a sales company that owns a **fleet of cars** for its staff to use. Some of the cars need replacing and Carlos needs to decide what **fuel** the new cars should run on.

   a) Suggest **two** factors he should consider in making his decision.

      1. ....

      2. ....

   b) Many people are concerned by the amount of fossil fuels that we use.
Suggest **one** reason why they are worried.

      ....

Q2 **Gasohol** is an alternative fuel that consists of a mixture of **two** substances.

   a) Circle the pair of substances that make up gasohol.

      hydrogen and carbon   petrol and ethanol   petrol and diesel

There's a hole in my gas.

   b) Suggest **one** advantage and **one** disadvantage of using gasohol as an alternative to petrol.

      ....

      ....

Q3 The box below shows part of an **advertisement** made by a car manufacturer for an experimental **hydrogen** powered car.

> **Be the first in your city to own a hydrogen-powered Wondercar.
> No pollution — the only thing coming out of the exhaust pipe is water vapour.**
>
> **Take a look at this graph showing the energy content of various fuels — hydrogen is way ahead of any other fuel.**

   a) What is the energy content of hydrogen in MJ per kg? ....

   b) Burning 1 kg of which fuel would release the most energy? ....

   c) 1 kg of hydrogen takes up about 9 times the volume of 1 kg of petrol.
Explain why this means hydrogen is less convenient to use as a fuel in cars.

      ....

   d) Suggest **one** other disadvantage of using hydrogen as a fuel.

      ....

Electromagnetic Waves

Q1   Jimmy is making a list of all the types of **electromagnetic waves** he can think of.
Circle the three types of wave that should **not** be on his list.

radio   sound   seismic waves   light   X-rays

microwaves   infra red   water waves   ultraviolet

Q2   All waves have a **frequency** and a **wavelength**.

a)   What units are used to measure wavelength? ....

b)   What does it mean to say that "the frequency of a wave is 25 hertz"?

....

c)   What happens to the energy of a wave as its frequency increases?

....

d)   The diagram shows a waveform.

Which of A, B or C is the length of one
whole wave?

....

Q3   Steven is doing his homework on **electromagnetic radiation**.

What can Steven say about the electromagnetic radiation being given out by a
light bulb? Complete the sentence by circling the correct word in each pair.

Energy / Matter **is being moved from one place to another without moving any** energy / matter.

Q4   Visible light is one type of **electromagnetic wave** — each **colour**
has a different **wavelength**. The diagram below shows some of
the colours in the visible part of the electromagnetic spectrum.

Red	Orange	Yellow	Green	Blue	Indigo	Violet

a)   Which has the shortest wavelength, red, green or indigo light? ....

b)   Does blue light have a higher or a lower frequency than yellow light? ....

c)   Which colour of light transfers the least energy from place to place? ....

Radio Waves and Microwaves

Q1 Phil is a **technician** at his local radio station. He knows that the **radio waves** that his station sends out can either be **transmitted**, **reflected** or **absorbed**.

a) Draw lines to match up the words with their correct meanings.

| Transmitted | | Energy is transferred from the wave to a substance. |

| Reflected | | The wave bounces off the boundary of a substance. |

| Absorbed | | The wave passes through a substance. |

b) It is not only radio waves that can be transmitted, reflected or absorbed — this happens to all electromagnetic radiation. Complete the following sentences by underlining the correct word.

    i) When microwaves heat up food, the energy of the microwaves is transmitted / reflected / absorbed.

    ii) You can see through a clear glass window. This shows that most of the light waves are transmitted / reflected / absorbed.

Q2 Molly makes a call on her **mobile phone** to Tara's mobile phone, some distance away. Complete the passage to describe how the **signal** travels from Molly's to Tara's phone.

X-rays   mast   pipes   microwaves   cables   satellite   nearest

The .... emitted by Molly's mobile phone are picked up by the nearest

mobile phone .... This transmits the signal through the central

mobile telephone exchange, where it passes to the mast .... Tara's

phone. That mast then emits the signal as microwaves, which are detected by Tara's phone.

Q3 The **longwave** radio band includes radio waves with wavelengths between **10 km** and **1 km**. The **shortwave** radio band includes radio waves with wavelengths between **120 m** and **11 m**. Use this information and your own knowledge to answer the following questions.

a) Which one of the following wavelengths of electromagnetic wave will bend around the Earth? Put a circle round the correct answer.

        5 km   **5 m**   **5 mm**

b) Write down **one** use of radio waves.

....

Top Tips: Radio waves with different wavelengths are used and transmitted in different ways. Some waves bend around the Earth's surface, some are reflected off a layer of the atmosphere, and others are sent directly to a receiver. All you need to do now is transmit this stuff to your brain.

Infrared and Light

Q1 Julia is experimenting with the **remote control** units for her family's TV set and DVD player. Remote control units work by sending a beam of **infrared waves** to a receptor on the television or other device.

a) Number the following types of electromagnetic waves in order of wavelength, from shortest to longest wavelength.

☐ visible light   ☐ ultraviolet waves   ☐ infrared waves

b) How can you tell that the remotes do **not** use visible light?

....

c) Use statements A-D to answer the following questions.

> **A** — Infrared waves can be transmitted through glass.
>
> **B** — Infrared waves can be reflected off walls or furniture.
>
> **C** — Infrared waves cannot pass through any solid object.
>
> **D** — Infrared waves cannot pass through opaque solid objects.

Opaque means the opposite of transparent. An opaque object is something you can't see through.

i) Julia changes TV channels using the remote control unit. She notices that even if she is holding it backwards it still works. What does this tell her about infrared waves? ....

ii) Julia's DVD machine is in a cabinet with a glass door. She finds she can use the DVD remote even when this door is closed. What does this tell her about infrared waves? ....

iii) Julia notices that if a magazine is placed in front of the receptor on the base of the TV then the TV remote cannot be used. The same happens if furniture or people block the path of the beam. What does this tell her about infrared waves? ....

I'll take that...

Q2 Bill, an **internet technician**, is fitting Sid's house with a broadband internet connection. Broadband internet uses **optical fibres**, which work using repeated **reflections**.

a) What sort of electromagnetic wave is usually carried by an optical fibre?

....

b) Give one use of optical fibres, other than in internet connections.

....

c) What is the difference between a fibreoptic cable and an optical fibre?

....

Risks and Benefits of Using EM Waves

Q1 Changes in **communication devices** has meant that some people can now **work** from **home**.

Give one social and one environmental impact of working from home.

Social impact: ....

....

Environmental impact: ....

....

Q2 Arthur is the manager of a British company whose **call centre** is based in **another country**. A **technological change** has made it possible for him to save money by using call centres in other countries where labour is **cheaper**.

Circle the letter next to the change that has made this possible.

A Introduction of fibre optic cables, which have made international phone calls cheaper.

B Development of the internet.

C Introduction of satellite TV channels.

D Introduction of Global Positioning System.

Q3 Kate is running a training course for hospital staff on possible **dangers** from X-rays, gamma rays, lasers, and ultraviolet rays.

She makes a table to show the risks from these four types of electromagnetic radiation.

Type of EM radiation	Risk
Lasers using visible light	
Ultraviolet	
X-rays	
Gamma rays	

a) Put the following statements into the correct boxes in the table.

Risk of cancer within the body.   Risk of skin cancer.   Low risk, but eye protection needed.

b) Label the boxes at each end of the arrow with the words "most dangerous" and "least dangerous".

Risks and Benefits of Using EM Waves

Q4   Read the following passage about **microwave ovens** and then answer the questions that follow.

> Microwave ovens are designed to generate microwaves to heat up food. So should we be worried that microwaves are cooking us, as well as our dinner?
>
> Well, probably not. The Microwave Technologies Association, which represents manufacturers, stresses that microwave ovens are lined with metal to stop microwaves getting out, and that there are regulations about how much 'leakage' is allowed. They also point out that the intensity of leaked radiation decreases rapidly with distance from the oven. So don't press your nose to the glass to watch your chicken korma reheating — gaze from a distance.
>
> We can't be certain that microwave ovens are absolutely safe — there might be long-term health problems that no one's spotted yet. But perhaps we should be more worried about other uses of microwave technology, like mobile phones. Mobile phones use microwaves — though of a lower frequency than those used in ovens. But mobile phones are very definitely _designed_ to emit microwaves (or else they wouldn't work) — so are they silently 'cooking' our brains?
>
> Interestingly, my mobile phone can still make calls from inside a microwave oven, with the door shut. If the microwaves from my phone are powerful enough to get out of the oven — with all its fancy shielding — then what on earth are they doing to my brain?

a)   Why are microwave ovens lined with metal?

....

b)   Why is it strange that the mobile phone can still make calls from within the microwave oven?

....

....

c)   Microwave ovens only came into use about thirty years ago.
What sort of safety problems might not have shown up yet? Circle the correct answer.

   communication   short-term   emission   leakage   long-term

d)   Do the microwaves used by mobile phones have a higher or lower frequency than the microwaves used in microwave ovens?

....

e)   Explain how microwaves used in microwave ovens can heat up food.

....

....

f)   Why does this method of heating mean that microwaves could be dangerous to the body?

....

Risks and Benefits of Using EM Waves

Q5 Cancer **tumours** are often hotter than the surrounding tissue. **Thermography** can be used to detect tumours by the increased amount of **infrared waves** they give off and is sometimes used as an alternative to **X-rays**. However, most doctors say it is less effective — not all cancers have a raised temperature and there are many reasons besides cancer that can cause hot spots in the body.

a) Suggest one reason why some people are afraid to have X-rays, even though they might detect cancer tumours.

....

b) Suggest one reason why thermography is not always effective in diagnosing cancer.

....

Q6 Colin is investigating the link between exposure to the **Sun** and **skin cancer**. He studied **15 000 people** for **10 years**. He recorded how **long** each of them had spent outside in the Sun on average each day and how many of them **developed skin cancer**. His results are shown in the table.

Hours spent outside	Number of cases
0-1	3
1-2	8
2-3	23
3+	40

a) What kind of harmful electromagnetic radiation is given out by the Sun?

....

b) Why can this kind of radiation be dangerous?

....

....

c) Plot a bar chart of the results on the grid provided.

d) Describe the trend seen in the results.

....

....

e) What percentage of patients in the study developed skin cancer?

....

Top Tips: Remember, just because electromagnetic waves are used in loads of today's gadgets and gizmos, it doesn't mean that they're completely safe. For your exam, it's just as important that you know the risks of each type of electromagnetic wave as well as the benefits.

Waves and Astronomy

Q1 Samantha is a physicist researching the **effects** that a **moving source of waves** can produce.

a) The diagram shows a moving source of sound waves. On the diagram, draw an arrow to show which way the source is moving.

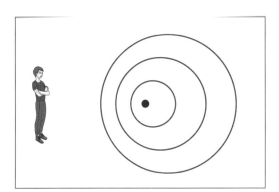

b) Circle the correct word from the pairs to complete the sentence.

> To the person on the left of the source,
>
> the wavelength seems **longer / shorter**,
>
> the frequency seems **higher / lower** and
>
> the pitch seems **higher / lower** than it
>
> would if the source was stationary.

c) Complete the passage by filling in the gaps.

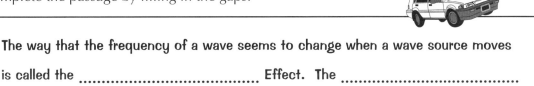

> **The way that the frequency of a wave seems to change when a wave source moves**
>
> **is called the** .... **Effect. The** ....
>
> **the source of the waves is moving relative to the observer, the stronger the effect is.**

Q2 Joel is an **astronomer** observing his favourite galaxy. The light from this galaxy is **blue-shifted**.

a) What does blue-shifted mean?

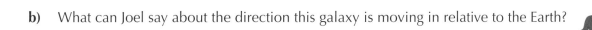

b) What can Joel say about the direction this galaxy is moving in relative to the Earth?

c) Complete the passage by circling the correct word from each pair.

> Light from galaxies can also be red-shifted. The more distant a galaxy is, the
>
> **more / less** the light from it is red-shifted. That suggests that each galaxy is getting
>
> further away from all the others — the **galaxy / Universe** must be expanding.

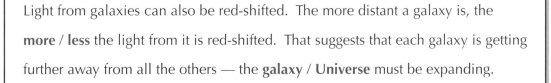

Mixed Questions for Sections 2.9 and 2.10

Q1   Rudy repairs and installs **TV aerials**. One morning after a heavy storm
he is called in by the Morris family. Their TV picture has gone fuzzy.

a)   The aerial on top of the Morris family's house has been knocked sideways by the storm.
Rudy adjusts it so that it points the same way as the other aerials in the street.
What are all the aerials pointing at? Put a circle around the correct answer.

the Sun   the nearest **TV receiver**   the nearest **TV transmitter**   the North Pole

b)   Rudy is concerned that there is less work for him than there used to be, because cable TV has
become more common. How is the signal for cable TV carried?

....

c)   Name one safety hazard that Rudy's work involves.

....

d)   Rudy says, "In the old days, if I was out on a job and someone wanted to book me in for another
job, all they could do was call and leave a message. It could easily be hours before I got back to
them. I lost a lot of jobs that way." Which invention has made it possible for potential customers
to reach Rudy all the time?

....

Q2   Here is a table showing the **frequencies** of three of Sally's favourite medium wave **radio stations**.

Name of station	Frequency (kHz)	Wavelength (m)
Froggart Radio	909	
CGP Live	1089	
Music Central	1215	

Below are the wavelengths that go with those frequencies.

275 m   **247 m**   **330 m**

a)   Write the wavelength for each station in the correct place in the table.

b)   Radio waves with very short wavelengths between 1 cm and 10 m pass straight through the Earth's
atmosphere. They are not affected by the layer of the atmosphere that reflects longer waves.

i)   Explain why radio astronomers are able to use ground-based telescopes to detect these
radio waves.

....

ii)   What observation have astronomers made that suggests that distant galaxies are moving away
from us very quickly?

....

....

Transport and Communication

Mixed Questions for Sections 2.9 and 2.10

Q3 Derek is a **lorry driver**. On his way back to the depot, he receives a call on the **C.B. radio** in his cab.

a) C.B. radios use **radio waves**. Radio waves can be grouped according to wavelength into long waves, short-to-medium waves and very short waves. Which type of radio waves:

i) bounce off a layer of the atmosphere? ....

ii) follow a curved path around the surface of the earth? ....

b) Derek has to stop suddenly when a cat runs out into the road. What **two** factors will affect his stopping distance?

1. .... 2. ....

c) During his emergency stop, Derek slows down from 24 m/s to 0 m/s. This takes him 6 seconds. Calculate his deceleration.

....

....

d) Derek's lorry runs on **diesel**, which is a hydrocarbon mixture. The table shows the composition and energy content of three types of transport fuel.

Name of hydrocarbon mixture	Number of carbon atoms in each molecule	Number of hydrogen atoms in each molecule	Energy content (MJ per kg)
Diesel	10 to 15	22 to 32	40.9
Petrol	5 to 9	12 to 20	42.7
Liquified Petroleum Gas (LPG)	1 to 4	4 to 10	46.0

i) Which fuel contains the most energy per kg? ....

ii) A hydrocarbon molecule has the chemical formula C_7H_{16}. Using the information in the table, state whether it is from diesel, petrol or LPG.

....

e) An alternative fuel is **gasohol**, made from petrol and ethanol.

i) Why is gasohol better than diesel in terms of pollution?

....

....

....

ii) Ethanol has the chemical formula C_2H_5OH. Is it a hydrocarbon? Explain your answer.

....

Mixed Questions for Sections 2.9 and 2.10

Q4 Emma works as a **computer network technician**. Her job is to install networks into offices using **fibreoptic cables** or by creating a **wireless network**.

a) Give one reason why a wireless network is more convenient.

....

b) Two common wavelengths of electromagnetic waves used in optical fibres are 850 nanometres and 1310 nanometres. (1 nanometre = 10^{-9} metres)

   i) Which of these two types of wave has a higher frequency? ....

   ii) Which carries more energy? ....

c) Explain why the process of sending data by optical fibres is very efficient compared to the way mobile phones transmit data.

....

....

....

Q5 Read the sentences about the **combustion of hydrocarbons**, then answer the following questions.

> • Two things can happen when a hydrocarbon is burned.
>
> • If there is enough oxygen available then complete combustion occurs.
>
> • If complete combustion occurs, carbon dioxide, water and heat are produced.
>
> • If there is not enough oxygen then incomplete combustion occurs.
>
> • If incomplete combustion occurs, other things as well as carbon dioxide, water and heat are produced. These other products can include carbon and carbon monoxide.

a) What is needed for complete combustion to occur? ....

b) Does the word equation below show complete or incomplete combustion?
Explain your answer.

   hydrocarbon + oxygen → carbon dioxide + carbon monoxide + carbon + water + heat

....

c) Does the balanced chemical equation below show complete or incomplete combustion?
Explain your answer.

   $$C_4H_{10} + 6\tfrac{1}{2}O_2 \rightarrow 4CO_2 + 5H_2O + energy$$

....

Transport and Communication